America's Last Chance

America's Last Chance

by Senator Gaylord Nelson

and the

Editors of Country Beautiful

Published by Country Beautiful Corporation   Waukesha, Wisconsin

COUNTRY BEAUTIFUL: *Publisher and Editorial Director:* Michael P. Dineen; *Executive Editor:* Robert L. Polley; *Senior Editors:* Kenneth L. Schmitz, James H. Robb; *Associate Art Director:* Wilbur A. Howe; *Art Assistant:* Roy Staab; *Associate Editor:* Lawrence Kenney; *Editorial Assistants:* Janice M. Puta, D'Arlyn Marks; *Contributing Editor:* Jerry Fetterolf; *Executive Manager:* Frank P. Morton; *Executive Director, Sales and Marketing:* Richard W. Stone: *Production:* Frank Bruce; *Circulation Manager:* Trudy Schnittka; *Administrative Secretary:* Donna Griesemer; *Editorial Secretaries:* Christine Maynard, Darcy Davies.

Country Beautiful Corporation is a wholly owned subsidiary of Flick-Reedy Corporation: *President:* Frank Flick; *Vice President and General Manager:* Michael P. Dineen; *Treasurer and Secretary:* Bok Robertson.

Frontispiece: Winter woods, northern Wisconsin. Photo by Martin Hanson.

CONTENTS

Introduction

As a boy growing up in a small town in northern Wisconsin, I fell in love with the out of doors — of which we seemed to have so much back in Clear Lake. To a boy, the trees seemed wondrously tall, the hills seemed very high, the waters seemed deep and pure and the wildlife seemed magically mysterious and plentiful.

It came as a shock to learn that these wonderful features in our great out of doors were all being threatened by the very progress which we had been taught in school to anticipate with such great expectations. It seemed impossible that anything done by man could actually destroy that wide world of nature. But I have been seeing it happen every day since then.

The biggest thing of all in this world outdoors was the sky. It was the sky I always thought of when they first taught us the meaning of infinity. It was into the open air we always wanted to escape. Who could have foreseen the day when man would be on the verge of turning the very air we breathe into poison?

But air pollution is just one part of the massive threat which faces our resources, all across the country and around the world. The same powerful forces which create the crisis of air pollution also are threatening our fresh water resources, our woods, our wildlife, and the scenic beauty of the nation. These forces are the rapid increase in population, industrialization, urbanization and scientific technology. More than any other public problem with which I am familiar, the threat to our natural environment poses a challenge to our system of self-government.

Partly because of my background, I have been preoccupied throughout much of my service as a state legislator, as Governor and as a United States Senator with the urgent need for preserving some significant part of our world of nature. Through the past decade of work in this field, I have come to the conclusion that the number one domestic problem facing this country is the threatened destruction of our natural resources and the disaster which would confront mankind should such destruction occur. There is a real question as to whether this nation, which has spent some two hundred years developing an intricate system of local, state and federal government to deal with the public's problems, will be bold, imaginative and flexible enough to meet this supreme test.

Our governmental system survived two world wars. It appears fully equal to compete with Communism in the struggle for world leadership. But, will it be adequate to cope with our own hell-bent drive to destroy our resources?

Let us just review for a moment what government has already done — or at least what it has allowed to be done — to our environment.

In much of the nation, we destroyed our forests. My own (Wisconsin) northland once had 200 billion board feet of white pine, one of the greatest concentrations of wealth anywhere in the world. We wiped it out in an eyewink of history and left behind fifty years of heartbreak and economic ruin. Forest fires raged through the slash left behind by the loggers. Crystal clear trout streams silted in. Hundreds of thousands of acres of land became tax delinquent and local units of government faced economic chaos.

Then we destroyed our rivers. Our cities and our developing new industries converted many of them into sewers, killing their fish, ruining them as a recreational resource, threatening the health of those who use them as a water supply.

At present, we are destroying our lakes. Our small inland lakes are being ruined by overdevelopment and by septic tanks and our mightiest bodies of water such as the Great Lakes are being slowly and steadily destroyed by municipal, industrial and shipboard wastes.

Strip miners and bulldozers raze our natural landscape. Pesticides, now being used at the rate of 700 million pounds a year, are spreading all across the land and the water, poisoning the soil, killing fish, and wildlife, and posing a potential threat to human health. DDT has been found in reindeer and penguins and its concentration is soaring as it progresses up the food chain — from water to plants, to fish to birds and presumably to man.

And now our factories, our automobiles, our public incinerators and our homes are filling the air with noxious gases and dangerous particles of pollutants at a terrifying rate. Thousands of deaths officially have been traced to air pollution and many thousands more almost certainly were caused by it. Polluted air is causing, or aggravating, bronchitis, asthma, emphysema, and lung cancer. It is making people more susceptible to pneumonia, and making it hard for elderly persons to breathe. It is interfering with the delicate systems by which the human body filters our irritants and makes use of the vital ingredients in fresh air. It is also making it difficult for pilots to see the ground as they approach our cities' airports.

Man lives on a limited, finite planet that spins in a mathematically precise orbit in the dead vacuum of space. The uniqueness of man's planet Earth is that it is the only body in the solar system capable of supporting life. Just how long it will be able to sustain life, however, is a question that is causing increasing concern to many scientists and ecologists. Our planet has only a thin veneer of soil that is supporting rapidly diminishing forests and a dwindling variety of animal species.

The scientists and ecologists have been warning for years that Earth's resources are not endless and that soaring population growth and blind disregard for the most vital resources of air and water could bring disaster because they believe that the end is virtually imminent.

Every major watershed in America has been polluted by the unbridled expansion of business and industry and by municipalities unwilling to clean their wastes adequately before dumping. Even the vast oceans, which make up three-fourths of the surface of the globe, face disaster and destruction. Man has looked to the oceans as the future source of food protein when the land becomes too crowded and too overworked to produce enough. But the pollution of the seas has become so serious that one noted ecologist has flatly predicted that the end of life in the seas could come in ten years.

Scientists already are studying mysterious events that point to a rebellion in nature. In the South Pacific, a marauding starfish is destroying coral reefs, and without these barriers many islands — including the Hawaiian group — will lie unprotected from the pounding seas. Scientists are guessing that dredging, underwater blasting, overuse of lingering pesticides or even radioactive fallout have killed the

Senator Nelson at a lake in Wisconsin.

starfish's natural enemies.

In the past year, other events have been observed that have brought death to thousands of creatures living in and around the sea. Some were killed by the ugly oil spills off the coasts of California and southern England. Some, however, remain unexplained — with only the dead fish, birds, clams, or crabs, tumbling by the thousands in the surf indicating that something serious was wrong.

The environmental threats have begun to jolt many Americans from their indifference and disregard for the severely limited natural resources of man. A recent Gallup Poll conducted for the National Wildlife Federation revealed that fifty-one per cent of all persons interviewed expressed deep concern about the effects of air pollution, water pollution and soil erosion and the destruction of wildlife and natural resources.

Each year new species of animals are added to the list of those soon to be extinct. Man in his arrogance appears to think that he can escape joining that list. The evidence is overwhelming, however, that it is much later that he realizes — that the species Man cannot long watch the animals disappear without seeing that his end, too, is coming. Man, ironically, may be the creature who left as his monument a planet nearly as incapable of sustaining life as its barren neighbors in the solar system that we are now so zealously exploring at fantastically greater costs that we are prepared to spend to preserve our own planet.

Man endangers certain species of animals
by invading and destroying their habitats.

1

The Price of Ecological Ignorance

Photo: Gordon Smith from National Audubon Society

I think one of the great lessons from these past few years of increased concern for quality in man's life and environment is that the "Piper" will be paid. We know far better now, for example, that whether we are developing a new drug or building a new expressway, we must take into account the human hazards as well as the benefits. Sophisticated as our technology has become, we know that in many crucial areas, there are voids, or only the most primitive beginnings of understanding. At the annual meeting in 1968 of the American Association for the Advancement of Science, Dr. Margaret Mead said: "We are altering man's environment in ways we do not understand and in ways which may be disastrous."

The examples are many. Scientists are concerned that many recently developed substances, such as artificial sweeteners and certain cosmetics, may be unknowingly affecting man's genetic structure or altering his reproductive capability. We cannot afford to wait to observe these possible effects in future generations. We must take the steps now to determine their consequences and protect against them. As a possible beginning is the legislation I introduced which establishes a national commission to investigate these potentially harmful effects.

In the past year, questions have been raised concerning our military's secretive development of chemical, biological and radiological weapons. We cannot afford not to know what these developments are, and what their implications are for the public health. Congress should take immediate steps to learn, for example, what safety precautions the army has taken in transportation of the lethal gases involved in its testing program.

Since World War II, the use and variety of pesticides has increased dramatically until today immense quantities of complex organic chemicals with multiple effects on and great persistence in the environment are being used by thousands of government and private organizations and millions of people. In this new situation, existing regulations and knowledge regarding pesticide uses and effects are inadequate. After more than two decades of television, we find we have far more questions than answers about its impact on society and on individual behavior patterns. We cannot afford not to greatly increase our understanding in this vital area.

Today, seventy per cent of the population of the United States lives in an urban environment in contrast with fifty-six per cent in 1930. In the year 2000, the figure will be eighty-two per cent. The way the public dollar is spent will continue to have considerable influence on the shape of that environment. For instance, the U.S. Government budget is proposing that we undertake a ten-year program to provide six million homes and apartments for low and moderate income families. We must take the care that is needed to insure that in any massive reshaping of our cities, we do not simply build in the ingredients for new slums and new human misery.

Opposite: Spray cans litter our parks and roadsides and introduce immense quantities of complex organic chemicals into the environment.

Photo: David Trumbel

Photo: Maurice E. Landre from National Audubon Society

Photo: Maurice E. Landre from National Audubon Society

Water pollution: in Dade County, Florida *(above)*, Key West, Florida *(top left)*, and in Illinois *(top right)*. All across the country people are demanding to know why the rivers, lakes and streams of the United States are either dead or in the process of being killed.

Each year, the list of environmental and technological problems becomes longer and more diverse. Wherever we turn, we are using technology to deal with our environment and with each other. The benefits have been great. In many respects, technology has led mankind to a new emancipation, but it has brought him suffering as well and is posing ever greater threats.

If in the future, what we call "progress" is going to be a blessing rather than, with increasing frequency, a curse, we must take steps now to redirect our technology so that it enhances rather than degrades man's health and well-being. This will require a new determination and sophistication, not only on the part of scientists and engineers, but also on the part of those involved in the institutions of our society — in government, industry, the universities — and on the part of individuals.

Beginnings have been made. Interest continues to build in the establishment of environmental and technological overview committees or councils in both the legislative and executive branches of government, and in the development of a national policy on the environment. Scientists continue to speak out on the dangers from technology and of the new environment it has produced. We see a new concern at international levels as well. The beginning made by the International Biological Program and

14

Above: Pittsburgh, before air pollution reforms were enacted.

the United Nations General Assembly's decision to hold a United Nations Conference on the Human Environment in 1972 are examples. Both efforts deserve our full support. Our job is to translate the new concern into effective action, even though it will be difficult.

The economic pressures to continue in the same old vein will be immense. The choices will be hard choices, for we do not want to eliminate technology but to reshape and redirect it. I am convinced though that we will have the public support to do what is necessary. There have been predictions recently of a taxpayers' revolt, and perhaps that will happen. I think it is just as good a bet, however, that a revolt is brewing over the continued introduction into our lives of new hazards and new nuisances under the label of "progress."

For too many years concern over pollution and conservation problems was only something that worried some outdoorsmen and conservationists. To most others, a little pollution of the water and air and a little destruction of the natural resources were a price that had to be paid for progress. In fact, outdoorsmen, conservationists and environmentalists found resistance when they came forward to stop a developer who was filling in marshes and the wetlands vital to many forms of animal and aquatic life or to stop a polluter of a major waterway.

The best the conservationist or outdoorsmen concerned over the natural resources could get was the derisive label, "birdwatcher" or "butterfly chaser." But things have changed and conservation of the environment is an issue that has come into its own time. All across the country and the world young people are demanding to know why the rivers, lakes and streams are dying or dead, why the air is thick with poisons and why the wildlife and the open public land are disappearing.

The general electorate is showing concern about conserving environment. In the last national general election, the voters proved that the environment is their grave concern. Voters in the Mojave Water District of California's San Bernadino County rejected a proposed coal-burning power plant, even though it would have contributed tax money to the district. The electorate simply did not want to increase the air pollution. In a suburb of Seattle, the residents had the choice between a wooded park and a nine-hole, community golf course. They chose the wooded section by a two-to-one vote.

In Maine, voters approved a $50 million bond issue to build a better municipal sewage-treatment plant, but turned down a $21.5 million bond issue to build more highways. In New Jersey, a $271

15

million bond issue for a massive clean water program passed easily. And, in New York State, a "Conservation Bill of Rights" amendment to the state constitution passed easily. It makes preservation of natural resources and scenic beauty a state policy. It also directs the State Legislature to write state laws to reduce air, water and noise pollution.

California and Virginia are working on similar laws and a similar amendment has been offered in the U.S. House of Representatives. This is a clear indication that, at long last, the nation wants and plans to see to it that our children and their children will have a clean, livable environment.

World-renowned ecologists, biologists, naturalists and scientists from every other discipline, of course, are alarmed by the rapidly accelerating deterioration of our environment. They are not simply alarmed that man's activities threaten to destroy his habitat and that of most other living creatures, but that he already has done irreparable damage — consequently our most urgent business is to stay the trend and then to reverse it.

In the long pull, no other matter before us is so important. We hope we might banish the bomb, wipe out poverty and achieve peace in the world —

but that will avail us little if we so degrade our environment that living in it is hardly worthwhile. We are moving rapidly on a course toward that end now and the obvious elements of approaching disaster are all around for anyone to see if he wants to look. There is a glimmering hope that man will abate his assault on the natural scheme of things if he understands what he is doing, and that understanding can come only from education which itself comes from strong and thoughtful leadership.

Even conservation, if it does not heed necessary ecological balances, can harm the environment. In 1887, a group of federal officials became concerned about protecting an important herd of four thousand mule deer living on the Kaibab Plateau in Grand Canyon National Park. As a part of the plan to protect the deer, the officials instituted strict hunting regulations and began eliminating all predator animals in the areas that might attack the herd.

From 1906 to 1931, unofficial records reported that hunters killed seven hundred mountain lions, thirty wolves, nearly five thousand coyotes and more than five hundred bobcats. Limited deer hunting permitted only the killing of bucks. The hunting restrictions and the elimination of the predators that normally helped keep the herd thinned worked

Above: A rotting cow is convenient feed for hogs in a rural dump in central Illinois.

Below: Pesticides, phosphates, oil or sewage effluence very likely killed this fossil-like fish.

better than anyone ever guessed. In fact, by 1924, park officials were faced with a number of stunning estimates that the deer herd had grown to 100,000.

The massive deer herd, competing for food with larger neighboring sheep and cattle herds, frantically stripped the plateau of vegetation, and the deer starved to death by the thousands. Within eight years, it was estimated that the herd had dwindled to some twenty thousand. The striking lesson the mule deer crisis teaches is that man invites disaster when he interferes with the balance of nature. It has been estimated that before the age of civilization, species became extinct at a rate of one per thousand years. Today, the rate is one lost species every year.

The World Health Organization estimates that, in the past one hundred years, man has pushed 550 species of mammals, birds and reptiles to the brink of extinction. Some 110 kinds of mammals have died out in the Christian era — seventy per cent of those losses occurred in the past century and forty per cent of the total in the past fifty years.

In this country, a number of creatures are on the endangered species list because their habitats are being unnecessarily destroyed and invaded by man. Among them are the magnificent eagle and the timber wolf. It is well known that the bald eagle has been critically threatened. What is not generally known is that the timber wolf is an endangered animal. There are fewer than eight hundred wolves in the forty-eight contiguous states; forty-five states have no wolves at all. The largest population of wolves in America — some five thousand — roam the Alaskan wilds.

But, if the present trend continues, the timber wolf population of that state could be extinct in a handful of years. There is a bounty for wolf hides in Alaska, and 5,593 bounties were paid during the four fiscal years ending June 30, 1968. It is evident that the Alaskan slaughter cannot continue for very long before the wolves are eliminated. Most of the wolf killing is part of a questionable sport with hunters using high-powered rifles, chasing wolf with an airplane until the animal is exhausted, then blasting bullets in the frantic beast. These same hunters have been known to consider it sporting to kill eagles in a similar way.

It is important to remember the words of the late conservationist, William Hornaday: "The wildlife of the world is not ours to dispose of wholly as we please. We hold it in trust for the benefit of ourselves and for equal benefits to those who come after us."

17

It is not generally known that the wolf is an endangered animal. There are fewer than eight hundred wolves in the forty-eight contiguous states, and in Alaska, where a bounty is paid for wolf hides, the remaining five thousand are being steadily slaughtered. (Photos: D.H. Pimlott)

2

Mankind and the Land

We are only now beginning to understand the subtle but unbreakable bond between man and his environment. As we confront the specific scars of physical degradation about us, and learn of the multitude of individual environmental insults which occur each day, we must carefully consider the role that man and his activities have played in producing this deterioration.

For almost a hundred years, we in the United States have been pursuing a policy of industrialization and urbanization. We have measured our success quantitatively and the mystical indicators on this quest have been the gross national product and the Dow-Jones industrial averages. Unfortunately, in our myopic pursuit of ever-increasing levels of production and consumption, we failed to detect and concern ourselves with the corresponding decrease in quality of life. And so, today, we find ourselves in the position of having to cope with the accumulated costs of years of unrestricted environmental despoliation.

In the headlong search for plenty, we are learning that we are ending up with less. We are discovering that man cannot live or act apart from his environment. The seemingly unrelated actions of another day and another place are erupting in a continuum of environmental abscesses — we sprayed the field to kill the pests and introduced a long-lived poison into our soil, water and bodies; we mined the coal to produce the power to feed the machines, and raped the landscape and gave our streams acid indigestion; we rushed to put up the suburbs and slashed away the ground cover and silted our waterways; we elevated the automobile to almost religious significance and multiplied the number of efficient pumps for pouring toxic substances into the air; and we channel industrial technology into creating new consumer products and processes and multiply the

number of chemical contaminants that can foul our air, water, land — and even our food.

The list of such shortsighted, terricidal actions is vast, and they all bore the label — "progress." The boastful nature with which these actions were initially proclaimed reminds me of the traveler in Shelley's poem, "Ozymandias," who came across a broken statue of the ancient king in the desert wastes. On the pedestal, the traveler found these words:

> "My name is Ozymandias, king of kings;
> Look on my works, ye Mighty, and despair!"
> [And the traveler saw that] Round the decay
> Of that colossal wreck, boundless and bare
> The lone and level sands stretch far away.

Will it be that the enduring monument to our acts of past bravado shall be the endless wasteland, the wastes of the productive-consumptive society stretching far away, without a man to record the scene in verse?

It is to be hoped that the new awareness of the ecological bonds between man and his environment and the increased knowledge of the burdens imposed by past actions will lead this country to a new operating ethic and will establish quality of life as a primary goal for all our people. There are some encouraging signs that this may occur. In particular, I have found an understanding, an awareness, and a desire among our younger citizens for environmental improvement. It is to be hoped that with their energy, dedication and, above all, greater ecologic knowledge, they may be able to persuade their elders to alter old attitudes. We do know, however, the movement to change ingrained patterns and habits will not be easy.

One of the most serious and pervasive "by-products" of American progress has been the pollution of almost every major body of water in this

Photo: Robert L. Olsen

Opposite: A stream bank planted with trees and grass can defend itself against erosion.

Construction sites must be thoughtfully
planned in order to avoid erosion.

country by wastes of all kinds, colors, shapes and
smells. We have polluted rivers in our urban areas so
badly that in some cases they are fire traps. But, we
also have polluted waters in the most remote areas
of the country. For decades, we have hidden our
eyes and hoped the growing pollution problems
would go away. But, in recent years, it has become
obvious and too gross to ignore. In fact, water
pollution has generated a national concern that with
each succeeding year is more insistent on immediate
and effective action. In our own region, we have seen
the voters of both Wisconsin and Michigan support
bonding issues in the hundreds of millions of dollars
to fund pollution cleanup. And, we have all seen the
intense citizen interest in Minnesota, Wisconsin and
Michigan over the fate of Lake Superior.

It has been gratifying to see the results when the
people really speak out as they have on the pollution
issue. Under precedent-setting federal acts, water
quality enforcement conferences have been held all
over the country in a national effort to stem the tide

of pollution. By mid-1969, forty-five federal-state
conferences had been held to abate the pollution of
interstate waters from Boston Harbor, the Potomac
River, and Lake Erie in the East, to Lake Michigan
and part of the upper Mississippi River in my region,
to Puget Sound and the Snake River in the West.

But perhaps the most important enforcement
conference yet is the one undertaken in May 1969,
to abate and prevent pollution of Lake Superior.
The conference was called by former Secretary of
Interior Stewart Udall after I had for several years
been urging such action either by the governors or
by the secretary. It is no small question of minor
concern. The dimensions and the values of this
natural resource are almost without parallel.

Let me describe Lake Superior in terms of what it
means not only to us, but to this country and to the
world. By volume, it is the third largest body of fresh
water on earth — almost three thousand cubic miles.
Only Lake Baikal of Russia and Lake Tanganyka of
Africa are larger. The shoreline of the lake stretches
2,976 miles and is perhaps Lake Superior's most
precious asset. The three states — Minnesota, Wisconsin and Michigan — share 1,427 miles of the
shore. Ontario, Canada, has 1,549 miles, making it
truly an international lake.

The federal report does a good job of describing
the sweep of the shoreline: "The wide sand beaches
of Whitefish Bay — the great parched dunes near
Grand Marais — the sheer cliffs of the Pictured
Rocks — the remoteness of the Huron Mountains —
the Apostle Islands — Split Rock Lighthouse — Isle
Royale National Park — and all that many miles of
primeval wilderness constitute a most valuable recreation and aesthetic resource."

But words aren't adequate for the feeling one has
standing on that ancient shore, sensing the whole
history of the earth unreel in the rocks, the cold
waters, the fog of even a summer morning. One
gains an impression then, rather humbly, of the
forces that created man — the same forces that just
as easily could sweep him away. Lake Superior is
pure as a well. So pure one can see a trout at depths
of up to five fathoms. So pure that one National
Water Quality Laboratory was located near Duluth,
Minnesota, in good part because this is one of the
few places where they would not have to import
water clean enough for their baseline work. On the
North American continent there is simply no body
of water to compare with this lake — in volume, in
purity, in value. And left to its own devices, with its
small drainage basin and infertile rock, Lake Superi-

Photo: courtesy Wisconsin Conservation Department

Lake Superior *(above and below)* has few equals in volume, purity and value.

Photo: courtesy Wisconsin Natural Resources Department

or would remain pure for thousands of years — unchanged — almost ageless. Yet, experience has shown us that there is little reason for comfort about the future of any resource in the world, especially in this age of expanding population, cities, industry and technology.

The federal report points out the delicacy of this body of water: "Its clarity is extremely susceptible to being reduced by pollutants. The addition of a few parts per billion of heavy metals will have a lasting deleterious effect on the lake. Sedimentation will damage fish spawning areas, which already are limited by the nature of the lake. The deep blue color, valuable esthetically and for tourists, can be changed by tiny particles in suspension. The quality of Lake Superior is so high, compared to other lakes, that early signs of damage may go undetected or may be excused as being insignificant."

Small changes wrought by man will set off a chain of events that could change this lake beyond present recognition in more ways than one. It is clear that this giant of a lake has an Achilles heel. It is a Goliath that can be slain by a David, though I doubt the event would be remembered as one of our heroic feats.

Above: A badly eroded stream bank in Wisconsin is in sharp contrast to the protected bank shown on page 20.

Right: Some sixty percent of America's highway system is not covered by any erosion control program.

Below: This bank in Ashland County, Wisconsin, along Lake Superior, was undercut after a spring thaw.

Above: A view of the Tennessee Copper Basin, photographed in 1943, shows what smelter fumes can do to an area's vegetation.

Maybe it would qualify for Ripley's "Believe it — or not." Or, maybe we could say: "We've finally moved this region into the mainstream of progress. We've polluted Lake Superior." Not too long ago in America that was the attitude — and it was once tolerated.

We haven't by any means polluted this lake yet. But, the danger flags are up — municipal wastes are being discharged directly into the lake or into the drainage basin from 93 cities, towns and districts. In many cases, treatment is at the outmoded primary level, or is non-existent, although pollution programs of the three states are underway, and, if followed, will improve the treatment. Industrial wastes are being discharged from sixty-one industries. In many cases, control is non-existent and entirely inadequate, and for some sources, abatement schedules have not yet been set by the states. I urge that schedules be set as quickly as possible so pollution from these sources can be eliminated.

Wastes are being discharged also from federal installations and facilities. Here again, controls are in some cases completely inadequate, and it is critical to the integrity of the federal program that pollution be stopped. Erosion in northwestern Wisconsin's red clay area has damaged valuable trout and recreational streams, discolored Lake Superior's waters off the south shore of the lake, and is damaging the lake's aquatic life. I urge state and federal officials to initiate a major program of soil conservation and stream-bank stabilization on south shore streams and watersheds based on recommendations of the Red Clay Committee.

Hundreds of commercial, sports and federal vessels are dumping untreated wastes directly into the lake. The U.S. Army Corps of Engineers continues to contribute to pollutions by dumping its harbor dredgings into the lake. Last year, the corps dredged one million cubic yards from harbors in Lake Superior and dumped most of it into open water. It is urgent that the corps studies and hearings produce results shortly.

As in any other major shipping or industrial area, Lake Superior faces the continued danger of disastrous oil leaks and spills, the effects of which we saw recently at Santa Barbara. On the Canadian side, there are indications that both American owned and Canadian paper mills are discharging untreated effluent directly into the lake. Effective protection of Lake Superior will require international cooperation — and perhaps international agreements — which I hope may be soon studied and recommended.

Legislation to permit federal assistance to fight pollution caused by erosion of stream banks and road banks is a dire necessity. Erosion of red clay soil along streams in northwestern Wisconsin has been cited among federal studies as a major source of pollution for Lake Superior. This is a perfect example of the need for this legislation. This kind of law would make possible large scale community erosion control projects which could be carried out for the entire course of a stream or for state and county roads unaffected by federal or municipal programs. The legislation would need to permit the Soil Conservation Service to furnish technical help

Left: By far the most striking example of natural erosion is the Grand Canyon.

Opposite: Former Secretary of the Interior Stewart Udall said man has failed to realize that "the soil was anchored to the land by grass."

and to share the costs of erosion control.

Stream-bank erosion along 300,000 miles of the nation's waterways destroys valuable land each year. The annual cost of removing sediment from stream channels, harbors and reservoirs is estimated at $250 million. In Wisconsin alone, there are 66,000 miles of stream banks and 24,000 miles of these stream banks have critical erosion problems.

As much as thirty per cent of the total sediment that pollutes streams, lakes and reservoirs in Wisconsin comes from stream-bank erosion. At least 1,000 of the 1,100 reservoirs in Wisconsin have filled with sediment to the point where they no longer serve their original purposes. About sixty per cent of America's highway system is not covered by any erosion control program. This needless erosion destroys valuable land, defaces the landscape, causes excessive highway maintenance costs, and pollutes many of our rivers and streams. Studies show that silt losses due to road-bank erosion run as high as 356 tons per acre per year in parts of Wisconsin. An estimated fifteen per cent of the silt polluting Wisconsin comes from this source.

We need expanded, comprehensive programs of federally supported ecological research. With our resources gradually disappearing, with our capacity to destroy the environment growing every day, we must know the impact on our environment of every step we take from now on. We must know in advance that wiping out forests destroys the soil, ruins lakes and streams, and even effects the climate and causes some agricultural crops to die. We must know that digging a canal to the ocean can admit sea lampreys and wipe out our lake fisheries. We must know that phosphates in detergents will fill our lakes with fast-growing algae.

Already pollution has all but destroyed many of our rivers and is on its way to completely destroying our oceans, lakes and fresh water supplies. Noxious gases fill the air, while industrial plants pour increasing amounts of harmful residue into our atmosphere. In addition, many of our nation's finest forests have been ravaged and all but destroyed. Vast tracts of land have been marred by strip miners and our precious landscape scarred forever.

Convincing evidence is accumulating rapidly from

every corner of the world that dangerous environmental contamination is resulting from the use of persistent pesticides. We literally are heading for environmental disaster. We must bring pesticide use in the United States into better perspective and completely re-evaluate existing regulations in light of the growing documentation of their harmful effects. The massive, often unregulated, use of highly toxic pesticides is seriously disrupting the ecological balance of nature. Most pesticides cannot distinguish between man's friends and man's enemies. They are lethal to beneficial insects and creatures as they are to destructive ones.

Fishery officials of the New York Conservation Department have reported that DDT is so concentrated in some New York lakes that it has completely halted reproduction of lake trout. Pesticide concentrations in New York trout are on the average slightly higher than the nineteen parts per million of DDT found in 1969 by the U.S. Food and Drug Administration in Lake Michigan coho salmon. The FDA seized 28,150 pounds of the salmon on the grounds that it was unfit for human consumption.

The DDT in the fatty tissues of New York lake trout was up to three thousand parts per million.

Reports of high pesticide concentrations like those in Lake Michigan and in New York State are a warning signal for all local, state and federal food-monitoring agencies to review closely pesticide concentrations in all food products susceptible to pesticide residues. This adds a note of extreme urgency to bring under adequate controls and necessary to ban the use of toxic, highly persistent pesticides such as DDT. Important health, as well as economic and social values are involved.

We now are moving rapidly on a collision course that will destroy man's habitat. These facts are grim and shocking, and we must now to halt this waste. Our natural resources are a precious commodity and we must begin prudently marshalling our efforts to stop this senseless destruction of our environment. If we are to do these things — if we are to save the natural resources of this land to sustain ourselves and future generations — then we must begin at once to develop better government programs and institutions to accomplish that life or death goal.

27

Photo: courtesy U.S. Department of Agriculture

3

Fouling the Waters: Lakes and Streams

Our growing population and expanding industries, the explosion of scientific knowledge, the vast increase in income levels, leisure time and mobility — all of these powerful trends are exerting such pressures on our natural resources that many of them could be effectively ruined over the next ten or fifteen years. Of all these developments, the most tragic and the most costly is the rapidly mounting pollution of our lakes and streams.

Each day, the water system of the nation — rivers, streams and lakes — collects the polluting runoffs of deadly pesticides, sewage and industrial wastes of all kinds. Nearly every watershed in the country, in even the most remote locations, has been touched in some way be pollution. Although the bulk of pesticide application is on land, especially long-lasting pesticides — like DDT and Dieldrin — are washed off by rains and carried into the nation's water systems. More than 1,640,000 fish were killed in a four-year period by pesticide pollution in the nation's waters — the result of pesticide spills or runoff and concentration in the waters.

Perhaps the tragedy of fouling our waters is more painfully apparent to a senator from a state like Wisconsin, bordered on three sides by the Great Lakes and the Mississippi, blessed with eight thousand inland lakes and hundreds of rivers and trout streams. But the bell is tolling for Wisconsin just as for all the nation.

A recent survey of twelve major river basins in southeastern Wisconsin found not a single one fit for even the partial body contact involved in fishing or wading. A competent governmental agency concluded that 754 miles of rivers in this region had been turned into open sewers. Beaches along Lake Michigan, a vast blue sea with seemingly limitless quantities of fresh water, are being closed to swimmers. A sordid ocean of pollution is pouring into the Mississippi River from the Minneapolis-St. Paul urban complex. Our small inland lakes are, one by one, becoming murky and smelly and choked with algae. Elsewhere, all across the nation, the same tragedy is being enacted, although in many areas the curtain already has come down. The waters already are ruined.

Every major river system in America is seriously polluted, from the Androscoggin in Maine to the Columbia in the far Northwest. The rivers once celebrated in poetry and song — the Monongahela, the Cumberland, the Ohio, the Hudson, the Delaware, the Rio Grande — have been blackened with sewage, chemicals, oil and trash. They are sewers of filth and disease. The Monongahela, which drains the mining and industrial areas of West Virginia and Pennsylvania, empties the equivalent of 200,000 tons of sulfuric acid each year into the Ohio River — which in turn is the water supply for millions of people who use and reuse the Ohio River water many times over.

What is happening to the Great Lakes offers still another prediction of things to come. The Lakes represent the largest collection of fresh water bodies in the world. Lake Erie, the sewer of Cleveland, Detroit, Buffalo and Toledo, now is almost a dead lake. Lake Michigan is on the way, with scientists warning that its phosphate level is rapidly approaching a critical point that could set off an explosive growth of algae and weeds that may never be

Foam indicates evidence of detergents containing phosphates that stimulate algae which use up oxygen vital to aquatic life.

Photo: courtesy Soil Conservation Service, USDA

Left: Though some plants have made reforms, water pollution by industrial waste is still rampant and becoming worse daily.

Below: Bay Beach, Green Bay, Wisconsin: Deterioration of our lakes is interfering with recreational uses.

stopped. Even Lake Superior, the cleanest of the Great Lakes, where a boatman still can dip a cup of drinking water directly from the lake, is threatened.

About six million pounds of waste products are discharged every day from U.S. industries and municipalities into the Detroit River. Twenty million pounds of measured waste constituents are discharged every day from U.S. waters of the Detroit River to Michigan waters of Lake Erie. Along the shores of Lake Michigan in Indiana and the Southern shore of Illinois, the waters are discolored by suspended and dissolved waste materials, in sharp contrast to the pleasing appearance of the rest of Lake Michigan. The waters of the Milwaukee area, particularly the lower Milwaukee River within Milwaukee County, Milwaukee Harbor and the adjacent waters of Lake Michigan are seriously degraded in quality. The waters of the Green Bay area, Michigan and Wisconsin, particularly the lower Fox River, and the southern end of the bay itself are seriously degraded in quality.

The problems that arise when attempting to find an answer to just the pollution of the Great Lakes is a good example of the kind of thing one runs into when attempting to grapple with the cancerous pollution problem. Sportsmen who want to see the waters stay pure for fishing and boating frequently object when they are told to install self-contained toilets on their boats. Industrial firms who rely on fresh, clean water argue that converting to non-polluting mechanisms is too expensive and makes it

impossible for them to compete with industries in other areas where such rules do not exist. Farmers want clean streams for their livestock, but they often ignore the fact that the pesticides they use on their crops run off into the streams to poison farm animals, fish and wildlife. There is concern about the threat to the environment, but it is the concern that someone else should clean up what he is doing first. That kind of attitude clearly will not solve the dilemma. The commitment must be nationwide — hopefully worldwide.

Deterioration of our lakes has become so bad that it is seriously interfering with recreational and other uses. A few of the lakes which already have suffered some degree of deterioration, in addition to the Great Lakes, are Lake Mendota and Lake Winnebago in Wisconsin; Lake Okeechobee in Florida; Lake-of-the-Woods in Minnesota; Lake Pepin in Minnesota and Wisconsin; Lake Champlain in New York and Vermont, Lake Washington in Washington; Lake Zoar in Connecticut; and thousands of other smaller lakes and ponds. Practically every state reports problems with algal growths, the problem being particularly severe in the Northern and Midwestern states.

The problems of lake deterioration — eutrophication, sedimentation, mineralization, salination — are directly correlated with the extent of private ownership — the greater the private ownership of the frontage of the lake, the more likely it is that the lake will have deterioration problems. Of course, there are many notable exceptions to this, for in many cases, private owners have practiced good shoreline management and saved lakes from destruction. The deterioration of a lake is due to complex interactions between man's activities and natural lake processes. All lakes undergo transformations over geologic time through which they gradually fill in and ultimately become dry land — in effect, they die. Man's activities accelerate and add new dimensions to these processes, however, so that what should take centuries or millenniums to occur may actually take place in a mere handful of years.

Agricultural, urban and commercial facilities and activities affect water supply and quality indirectly by disturbing shoreline and watershed vegetation and drainage and directly by water withdrawals and waste disposal. In turn, these changes disturb or destroy the conditions of breeding and survival of fish, animals and birds, resulting in substantial changes in wildlife populations. Of course, esthetic quality of the natural land around the lake is adversely altered, or completely destroyed, by all of these changes. The end result of this process of spoliation is that the lake becomes a stinking cesspool, filled with pollutants, trash and mud, devoid of animal and plant life and practically useless to man.

One of the important lake processes affected by the large quantity of wastes from cities, farms and factories is eutrophication. Such wastes contain a high proportion of phosphates and nitrates from detergents, artificial fertilizers, manufacturing raw materials and sewage. Domestic and industrial detergents, containing up to fifty per cent by weight of phosphate compounds, are responsible for a substantial part of this substance found in these wastes. The phosphates and nitrates serve as plant nutrients and encourage an overproduction of algae. Eventually, if biological enrichment continues too long, decaying algae take oxygen out of the water and release noxious and even poisonous substances. These extensive algae blooms also disrupt currents and waves, encourage the build-up of sediment and impede evaporation and aeration.

Photo: courtesy Wisconsin Natural Resources Department

31

Photo: Paul Toppelstein-Cleveland Press

Above: A Public Health Service study revealed that virtually no conventional aquatic life exists in Cleveland's harbor.

Below: A tidal basin in Washington, D.C., reveals offensive debris and litter dumped from passing pleasure boats.

Photo: courtesy National Park Service

Above: Straw absorbs oil allegedly spilled by a Scottish freighter into Lake Michigan at Chicago's Navy Pier.

Right: Some streams have managed to escape the serious pollution that fouls every major river system in America.

Below right: Utter disregard or indifference toward the purity of water has become part of the American way.

Below: One pound of phosphate will propagate seven hundred pounds of algae, which blooms, dies and becomes a pollutant.

Chicago Tribune Photo

Photo: Maurice E. Landre from National Audubon Society

Photo: courtesy Federal Water Pollution Control Administration

Above: An economical sewage treatment lagoon at Wayne, Nebraska.

National attention has been centered on once beautiful Lake Erie, the great lake which is the recreational front yard of Buffalo, Cleveland, Toledo and Detroit and which supplies water for ten million Americans. A Public Health Service survey of Lake Erie made the shocking discovery that in the 2,600 square mile heart of the lake, there was no dissolved oxygen at all in the water. The lake in this vast area could support no desirable aquatic life, only lowly creatures such as bloodworms, sludgeworms, sowbugs and bloodsuckers. Along with the germs and industrial acids which pour into Lake Erie are millions of pounds of phosphates, a major ingredient in detergents. Each pound of phosphate will propogate seven hundred pounds of algae. Beneath the waters of this great lake, largely hidden from sight, a hideous cancer-like growth of algae is forming. As algae blooms and dies, it becomes a pollutant itself. It robs the lake of still more oxygen — and it releases the phosphate to grow into another crop of algae.

Lake Erie is a product of its tributaries. A Public Health Service study of these American sewers is horrifying to read. The Maumee River flows from Fort Wayne, Indiana, through Defiance and Napoleon, Ohio, and on to Toledo, where it joins the lake. Even as far upstream as Fort Wayne, the river has insufficient oxygen to support anything but trash fish and lower organisms, and as it flows toward Lake Erie, conditions get steadily worse. The count of coliform bacteria runs as high as 24,000 times the allowable maximum under federal drinking water standards. The concentration of carbolic acid — a by-product of steelmaking — runs up to 137 times the allowable maximum. A packing company dumps 136 pounds of oil per day into the Maumee River. A plating company dumps thirty-eight pounds of cyanide per day.

Defiance, Ohio, closes its sewage plant entirely for one or two months each year, and all its raw sewage goes directly into the Maumee. Below Defiance, a foundry dumps cinders and ashes into the river. The Maumee is joined by the Auglaize River, which is even more polluted than the Maumee and is especially rich in ammonia compounds. At Napoleon, Ohio, the city draws its drinking water from the sordid Maumee and a soup company draws off ten million gallons a day for soup processing. (The firm assures me that its modern water treatment plant, complete with carbon filters, can "polish the water to a high quality.")

Below Napoleon, things get really bad. Forty per cent of the samples taken by the Public Health Service showed presence of salmonella, an intestinal bacteria that can cause severe illness. As the Maumee flows into Lake Erie at Toledo it gets its final killing dose of pollution — the effluent from the Toledo sewage plant, and what the Public Health Service describes as "oil, scum, metallic deposits and toxic materials."

35

Sand dunes, woods and miles of spotless beach mark
the John Michael Kohler State Park near Sheboygan, Wisconsin.

Another Lake Erie tributary, the Cuyahoga River,
which flows into the lake at Cleveland, was described by the Public Health Service as "debris-
filled, oil-slicked and dirty-looking throughout."
It is loaded with coliform bacteria and salmonella. It
is so polluted with oil that it frequently catches fire.
Structures known as "fire breaks" have been built
into the river to fight these blazes. In Cleveland
Harbor, the Public Health Service could find virtually no conventional aquatic life. However, the
sludgeworms which thrive on organic matter were
well represented — 400,000 per square meter on the

Photo: courtesy Wisconsin Conservation Department

harbor bottom.

That is the story of Lake Erie and, although it is so shocking and disgusting as to deserve urgent national attention, it is not unique. Southern Lake Michigan, ringed with oil refineries, steel mills and municipal sewage outfalls, may be even worse. Scientists estimate that it would take a hundred years to replace the polluted water of southern Lake Michigan, and some consider the pollution in this area irreversible. We have our own Wisconsin pollution scandal in Green Bay, a magnificent recreational body of water in northeastern Wisconsin, widely known as a yachtsman's paradise and site of a multi-million-dollar resort industry. This "Cape Cod of Wisconsin" is threatened with ruin by a tide of pollution which is moving up the bay at the rate of more than one mile per year. The pollution comes from rivers such as the Fox, the Peshtigo, the Oconto and the Menominee, which drain large areas of Wisconsin and northern Michigan.

In the deepening national crisis facing our rivers and lakes, a dramatic new pollution source is developing — the massive discharges of heated water from nuclear power plants. On Lake Michigan alone, seven nuclear power plants, several with capabilities larger than any in the history of power generation, are scheduled to be in operation by the mid-1970's. Together with the output of existing plants fueled by coal and oil, the higher volume of expelled, heated water will raise the temperature of all Lake Michigan by several degrees in the next few decades.

In addition to the threatened change in the taste and smell of drinking water near some of the plants, the delicate chain of Lake Michigan aquatic life, already severely threatened by other pollutants, could be further upset. Algae growth is already a problem that could be greatly increased by the warmer water. Yet, incredibly, not one of the plants is installing cooling towers to reduce environmental impact of the heated water on this vital segment of the Great Lakes chain — a major resource of international importance.

On a nationwide basis, 120 nuclear power plants will be installed within the next six years. By 1980 the electric power industry — with both nuclear and fossil fuel plants — will be using one-fifth of the total fresh water runoff in the United States for cooling. But the Atomic Energy Commission, which is charged with regulating the development of the nuclear power plants, said it has absolutely no responsibility to assure that the gigantic heat discharges will be controlled.

The experience with new and old sources of pollution in Lake Erie, Lake Michigan and all the Great Lakes has convinced many experts of this chilling fact: It is a definite possibility that the Great Lakes — the greatest single source of fresh water in the world — could be effectively destroyed by pollution in the years ahead. If this were to happen, it would be the greatest natural resource disaster in modern history.

4 Fouling the Waters: The Ocean and Wetlands

Perhaps man with his rampaging breeding and indifference has reached the point where much of the world he lives in will be nothing more than an area of poisonous waters and choking air surrounded by mountains of garbage and debris. With many municipalities already faced with a monumental problem of garbage disposal, it is estimated that every man, woman and child in this country is now generating five pounds of refuse a day from household, commercial and industrial uses. This refuse adds up to more than 365 billion pounds a year in the United States alone.

Instead of using the country's impressive technology — which made it possible to land man on the moon and develop super-mechanical devices capable of solving astronomical problems — the typically American approach is to take the easy way: simply dump the debris and garbage in the ocean. Why shouldn't the municipal governments, business and industry believe the ocean would be a good dumping place? The sea bottom already is being used for dumping radioactive wastes and some thoughtful military bureaucrat recently decided it would be a great place to dump 12,000 canisters of obsolete nerve gas.

Previous dumping may have caused some of the massive sea kills I have described. The oceans are not a limitless funnel that takes the chemical wastes and other debris to a magical "somewhere else" where they can be forgotten. More than twenty years ago, Los Angeles found that its beaches were contaminated and had to be closed to bathers because the city was not sterilizing its sewage. It also was discovered that wastes pumped by England into the North Sea were damaging Grand Banks fisheries off Newfoundland. The Japanese, concerned about their valuable fishing industry, have wisely banned dumping sewage into the sea.

Oil pollution from an offshore rig leak fouls the ocean.

Dump, Estuaries

Photo: courtesy National Park Service

Our undersea domain is not the only ocean area that is threatened. Landward, our coastline environment is becoming an unmanageable tangle of conflicting, polluting uses that eliminate wetlands, destroy shellfish and other valuable sea life in sensitive estuaries, wipe out beaches with unwise development and degrade the natural values that make our coastline areas perhaps the most vital recreation resource in the nation.

The nation's capital itself stands as an example of the desecration of environment. Washington is a non-industrial city of broad avenues and vast expanses of green. In that, it is unique among major American cities. But like all other American cities, the pressures caused by a rapidly growing and crowded metropolis are evident. The Potomac River, described by early explorers as "*teeming*" with fish and wildlife, is little better than an open sewer. Estuarine destruction continues within sight of the nation's capitol buildings as wetlands are filled. The river is totally unsafe for swimming and questionable for fishing, and a haze of pollution hangs in the air with many tons a day added by airplanes alone. Recreation space is scarce and the District of Columbia is running out of room to dump its garbage.

With demand for the nation's severely limited open space facilities already exceeding capacity, it is particularly disturbing to see Everglades National Park, one of the most valuable features of the National Park System, in grave danger of imminent destruction. In 1934, the 1.4 million-acre park was set up by Congress to be "protected in perpetuity" as a unique sub-tropical wilderness in rapidly developing south Florida. The concept, "protected in perpetuity," in the National Park statutes always has been comforting because it seems to rule: "Here is where we draw the line. Here we are endowing a priceless natural resource with a sanctity not unlike that of a church."

But as is so often the case, the commitment of words and statutes is being swept away by the frenzied pursuit of profit. The Everglades Park is on the brink of destruction, final and complete. One conservationist predicts that within ten years, there will be an announcement by the federal government that the park is no longer worthy of the name and, therefore, it will be abandoned like an old military base, in the interest of economy.

It would be particularly appropriate for the government to pronounce the doom of the Everglades

Photo: courtesy National Park Service

because it has permitted federal agencies — specifically, the U.S. Army Corps of Engineers — to work in direct opposition to the intent of Congress, to endanger the park. In 1962, the Corps of Engineers constructed a levee across the principal natural drainage way to the Everglades from the north and blocked the flow of water into the park for two years.

That water shortage brought the death of multitudes of fish, wildlife and flora and began an unnatural succession of changes which may alter the unique ecology of the Everglades for all time.

The only thing that saved the park was a dramatic increase in rainfall in recent years, but that can be only a temporary respite. Conservationists supported the Corps Flood Control Project, provided the Corps would insure that the flow of water would not be cut off from the park. Without that protection, it is clear that the water, the life blood of the park, will be choked off by the escalating, industrial-municipal water demands of southern Florida or by drought. Wealthy land developers of south Florida won't be happy until every square mile of the Everglades is dredged, filled, put under the blade of

Wide World Photos

Above left: People made brave but largely futile attempts to soak up with straw the many gallons of oil that leaked into the ocean waters off Santa Barbara, California in 1969.

Above right: On August 18, 1970, the Army scuttled this World War II Liberty ship in sixteen thousand feet of water 282 miles off the Florida coast. Its cargo: over twelve thousand nerve gas rockets enclosed in concrete vaults.

Left: Man is a "user," not a "consumer," and he must begin to learn how to dispose sensibly of the things he uses.

Photo: Gordon S. Smith from National Audubon Society

41

Photo: George Komorowski from National Audubon Society

Two geese browse along the edge of a clean lake *(above)* while a flock of pintail ducks *(opposite top)* takes wing from the Tule Lake Refuge in California. *Left and opposite:* Two oil-soaked victims of offshore spills: a dead dovekie and a doomed, bewildered gannet.

Photo: Bob Baldwin

Photo: courtesy Water Pollution Control Administration

Photo: George Komorowski from National Audubon Society

One of eight thousand oil wells that have been drilled on the outer continental shelf,
this rig off Santa Barbara is shown spilling oil into the ocean.

Photos: courtesy National Park Service

a bulldozer and subdivided into suburban lots around dead lagoons stocked with fish from some place else.

The massive oil leak off Santa Barbara, California, which killed and continues to kill fish and sea fowl could be the first dramatic warning of complete destruction for the seas and continental shelf areas of Earth. Other commercial ventures are under consideration as developers look into the possibilities of rich returns from moving parts of crammed megalopolis to floating cities. One developer is planning a floating jetport in the ocean waters off New York City. Such a facility might well be beyond the reach of enforcement of any federal agency regulations. The one heartening sign so far has been the courageous move by the State of New Jersey to freeze all action on purchase, lease, and use of state lands on coastal tidal waters until completion by the state of a master plan for managing the coastal environment.

The same freeze should immediately be adopted for public coastal lands on the Atlantic and Pacific coasts, the Great Lakes and the Gulf of Mexico. The federal government should halt all aid for development that would affect this environment until plans meeting national criteria are developed. And, on the outer continental shelf — the vast undersea region extending beyond the coast — the Secretary of the Interior should grant no more leases of any kind until similar environmental criteria can be developed to protect this vital last frontier.

To date, eight thousand oil wells have been drilled on the outer continental shelf. And little mention is made of the fact that the outer shelf is really 823,000

Future generations may very well inherit a world with poisonous waters and choking air and mountains of garbage and debris.

square miles of undersea public domain, owned by the people of the United States. This public domain once was much greater, but, in 1953, with the Submerged Lands Act, Congress gave outright, to the states, the first three miles of offshore seabed. Today, greedy over the prospect of trillions and trillions of dollars in potential minerals, the East Coast states are banding together to fight the federal government in court for the undersea booty beyond the states' three-mile territory in a mad scramble for the public domain frontier.

Unfortunately there is a great deal of confusion and litigation concerning whether various ocean waters are public, private, national or international. It seems to be a wild, utopian dream that the world will be able to face the threat to the oceans in any reasonable way in the face of the fact that various government jurisdictions in this country cannot get together to develop responsible control programs for a simpler problem — domestic pollution. Without agreements or strong regulations, the massive business and industrial corporations are at it again. This time it is frontier days on the high seas, and it's damn the environment, full speed ahead.

5

New Priorities: Cleaning Up

Looking at the record of destruction by pollution we ask — is all this pollution necessary because of our vast urban and industrial growth? Can we write it off as a problem that we can't allow to interfere with progress? No, we must stop this senseless destruction of our irreplaceable resources. We can do it. We have the technology. All we have lacked is the determination to provide financial resources.

It has been estimated $30 billion will be required before the year 1975 for the construction of municipal and industrial treatment works, for the construction of sanitary collection sewers, and for construction of industrial cooling plants. More than $8.7 billion is needed for the construction and replacement of municipal treatment facilities.

All across the country, states, cities and towns have moved to meet the challenge of cleaning our waters and stemming the tide of pollution. Water quality standards and pollution abatement programs for interstate waters have been submitted to the Interior Department for approval by all fifty states. Work is also progressing in the states on establishing standards and abatement programs for intrastate waters.

I am tremendously pleased with progress made in interstate pollution conferences, too. I am convinced that meaningful pollution abatement programs can best be developed in no other way than through state-federal conferences.

In January 1968, a state-federal pollution conference on Lake Michigan was convened in Chicago. The first session of the conference was devoted mainly to analyzing and identifying the pollution problems of that great body of water. The picture painted was not a rosy one; rather, it was one of a beautiful fresh water resource seriously threatened by a wide variety of pollutants including wastes from vessels and ships, inadequately treated industrial and municipal wastes, persistent pesticides and polluted dredging spoils.

The mood of the conferees, representing the states of Wisconsin, Michigan, Indiana and Illinois, was one of concern about the problem and of willingness to cooperate in setting up a meaningful pollution abatement program for Lake Michigan. At the second session of the conference later that year, the conferees unanimously adopted twenty-six recommendations designed to save Lake Michigan.

Our program to save Lake Michigan is critical. We must move ahead boldly and decisively, for this may well be our last chance to save this irreplaceable water resource. In the future, we must not only monitor the Great Lakes constantly, but also we must keep ahead of all technical developments which might directly or indirectly have an effect on those waters.

Industry faces major problems in its efforts to treat its wastes and halt the pollution of our waters. Industrial wastes are much more complex and difficult to handle than municipal wastes. A program of grants to industries to help them develop effective means of treating their wastes is very much needed. The problem with industry goes beyond this. Once satisfactory waste treatment systems are developed, industry will be faced with the enormous costs involved in installing these pollution abatement facilities. I hope that the appropriate congressional committees will act on this critical problem.

The task of cleaning up our nation's waters will not be an easy one. States, cities and towns across

Opposite: Cleaning up our nation's waters will be a costly task.

Above: Chicago health officials became sick while taking samples from this waste outlet into Lake Michigan.

this great nation have indicated their willingness to do their share of the job. Now it is up to the federal government to do its part. It is important that the federal government meet and improve its commitment to the critical problem of controlling the pollution of our waters. I am convinced that the dramatically increasing gap between authorizations and appropriations will actually put the state and local water pollution control programs — the backbone of the national effort — in danger of collapse.

The ultimate solution, of course, is going to have to involve a great deal more federal funding than is presently going to the states for pollution control. This is a matter which should be given top priority by both the Administration and the Congress.

America must replace the war in Vietnam with a war on unsolved problems of this nation. As we enter the last third of the twentieth century, the central challenge we face as a democratic society is to turn the powerful forces unleashed by scientists and technology to our benefit instead of to our misfortune, to provide quality as well as quantity in our everyday lives.

The very quantity which our talent and wealth has produced is exacting tremendous cost from the quality of life which we as a society pursue. It can be measured in very human terms — by hungry children, the sick who suffer without benefit of medical consultation and treatment, frustrated commuters, families who can't find a place to hike in the out-of-doors, or a clean lake for their boat.

A further tragedy is that the benefits of our advanced technology often have fallen far short of reaching not only the poor, but the well-off.

To wage this new war, the nation's scientists must be mobilized with the same urgency, the same national commitment as in World War II when our scientific capability was used with tremendous effectiveness for the Manhattan Project, for the conquest of space, for the development of the proximity fuse, and for radar. The scientist, the technician, the engineer have given us the knowledge and the tools which have made this nation great. Now they must help us to harness science and technology to fashion the kind of life and environment which will obtain a better, more meaningful condition for society and

Above: Hot water from a new building flows directly into Lake Michigan, an example of thermal pollution.

Left: Industrial pollution fills the James River as it passes through historic Lynchburg, Virginia.

Photos: courtesy Wisconsin Natural Resources Department

An oxygen-testing kit (*above*) and a portable
water monitoring station (*opposite bottom*)
are two examples of how technology can begin
to improve the quality of our lives. If water
pollution control is to succeed, we must be
continually aware of the problem (*opposite top*).

the individual man.

We must apply our scientific know-how to the analyses and solutions of our social problems with the same creativity with which we have applied it to the waging of war, and the keeping of the national defense.

We must use the same ingenuity that has provided the miracle of heart transplant surgery to create systems to deliver medical care to the very heart of the ghetto and to the most isolated communities of rural America. Creation of a National Health Corps involving professionals, paraprofessionals and local volunteers could accomplish such a needed task of providing quality for lives.

I am convinced that the vast energies of this country are waiting only to be tapped in a national mobilization to conquer our social and technological ills. Millions of Americans in the past decade have made themselves heard and felt in the struggle to halt the mindless degradation of our environment.

Unfortunately, many decisions already have been made that will be felt through the full decade of the 1970's. One of those decisions was that this nation begin the development of a supersonic transport.

Above: Student seminar held by Water Pollution Control Administration.

Chicago Tribune Photo

Despite warnings that the SST would be too expensive to develop to ever bring a proper economic return and that the sonic boom following the shrill flight of the massive aircraft would be environmentally dangerous, the decision was made, never-the-less to invest eventually $1.3 billion toward construction of two prototypes.

The arguments against the development of the supersonic airplane adequately counter the arguments that it is necessary. There are those who argue that the American manufacturers will lose money on the world market because airlines will be buying SST's from the French. It is doubtful, however, that enough planes will be sold to bring a return on the government's $1.3 billion investment. There is additional concern that, for the SST to be commercially profitable, it would have to have a continual federal subsidy.

The sonic boom appears to be the most intolerable aspect of the big jet that will have a top speed of 1,800 miles per hour. There is no scientific evidence that the dangerous, shattering sonic boom that will follow the jet ever can be overcome. Even the staunchest supporters of the aircraft do not foresee flying at supersonic speeds over populated areas, and all present projections are for SST service only over oceans and trans-polar routes.

It has been pointed out that the sonic boom of the SST at contemplated typical altitudes of fifty thousand feet can be of window-breaking intensity on the ground. At sixty thousand feet, the surface boom still can be nerve-shattering. The areas of sonic boom noise at those altitudes will be heard and felt across a fifty-mile-wide strip on the surface. Even though the irritating noise will be limited to ocean or arctic areas, many scientists are concerned that the noises would cause environmental threats to polar wildlife or to men on ships in polar regions.

The best arguments against the SST, however, probably come from the presidential science adviser, Dr. Lee A. DuBridge:

On the whole, I come out negative on the desirability for further government subsidy for the development of this plane. . . . Any technological benefits which would accrue from its further development, either for civilian or military purposes, would seem minimal.

Granted that this is an exciting technological development, it still seems best to me to avoid the serious environmental and nuisance problems; and, the government should not be subsidizing a device which has neither commercial attractiveness nor public acceptance.

And, for all too long, we have granted without question all that is asked in the name of national defense. Even now, the pressure from the burgeoning defense budget and the war are forcing cutbacks in critical domestic programs. For instance, the federal government in fiscal year, 1970, spent only $42 million on research, development and demonstration for the whole range of the effects of pollution in lakes, in the air, in our ecological systems, on Man. By contrast, Congress the same year was asked to appropriate billions for an anti-ballistic missile system to defend two offensive missile sites. While we spend only $1.5 billion annually in federal funds for research contracts and grants for our universities and colleges, we have spent more than $4.1 billion in the U.S. Army alone for missile systems that are no longer deployed.

We hear endless talk about our defense posture in the world. But, what about our posture in science, in education, in environmental control, and in health? We can spend it all on defense and leave nothing to defend. The conclusion is clear, it is not only the scientists who must wage the new war in America, it is the politicians in the Congress — a Congress that can make history if it is willing to tangle with that toughest of all problems — putting first things first, by setting priorities straight.

If we act and win, we will be setting a new benchmark for progress. It won't be GNP. It won't be mere quantity. It will be achieving a quality of life for America. That is the new challenge for science and technology, and for everyone in America.

Below: Students demand a halt to mindless pollution of the earth.

By burning fossil fuel at an ever increasing rate, man releases carbon dioxide into the atmosphere more rapidly than it can be taken up by green plants or dissolved in the oceans.

6

Man and Breath

There is almost no way to escape the poisons of pollution. Day after day the thin envelope of air that surrounds the earth is mixed with the belching smoke and soot of tens of thousands of industrial smokestacks and home incinerators along with deadly fumes from millions of automobiles, buses and trucks exhausting gases and lead particles from fuel into the air. Just how long the atmosphere will be able to absorb these pollutants cannot be predicted accurately. Air pollution is a massive problem of the greatest urgency. It is utterly unrelated to traditional political boundaries. It can be nationwide, even worldwide, in its effects. It taxes the technical knowledge of our leading scientists. Clearly this is one public problem which cannot simply be left to local government to handle as it sees fit.

Many of our air pollution problems are regional in nature. The boundaries of regional air pollution problems are determined partly by geography, partly by the patterns of air movements, partly by the pattern of urban sprawl. Our scientists tell us that air pollution does some $10 to $12 billion damage every year. It damages farm crops as much as a hundred miles from the source of the pollution. It blights pine trees, kills orchards, damages orange groves and grapevines and ruins spinach. It corrodes metals, weakens fabrics, discolors paint, etches glass, cracks rubber and spreads filth over everything. It turns white snow black, and it soils wash on the line before it even can be worn. These are the things we can see with our eyes, breathe with our lungs and feel with our hands. But, up there in the once-blue sky, concealed behind a blanket of smog, things are happening which no average person can see or feel.

A Cornell University scientist, Dr. LaMont Cole, testified before our Senate Interior Committee on my bill to authorize research into ecology — the relationship of all the different elements in our environment. Dr. Cole said: "Man is burning fossil fuel at an ever increasing rate, and it is probable that more than half of the fuel ever burned by man has been burned in this century. One result of this is to release carbon dioxide into the atmosphere more rapidly than it can be taken up by green plants or dissolved in the oceans and eventually precipitated. ... It appears probable that the carbon dioxide content of the atmosphere has increased by at least ten per cent since the turn of the century. Atmosphere carbon dioxide," Dr. Cole continued, "is believed to have drastic effects on climate and there are now diametrically opposed hypotheses as to what effect this change may have.

"One hypothesis predicts that the world temperatures will increase and melt the ice caps from Greenland and Antarctica, thus raising the sea level and drastically altering the world's coastline. The other hypothesis contends that precipitation, including snowfall, will increase so much that glaciers will start to advance and bring on a new ice age." The scientists also remind us that this orgy of fuel burning — which stokes the fires of American industries and powers our autos and planes — is using up oxygen at an accelerating rate. Again, Dr. Cole testified: "The only reason the earth's atmosphere contains oxygen for us to breathe and with which to burn fossil fuels, is that oxygen is constantly being given off by green plants. If we reach the point at which the rate of combustion exceeds the rate of photosynthesis, the oxygen content of the atmosphere will start to decrease — I suspect that we are close to the critical point. . . .."

Scientist after scientist offered similar testimony at our Ecology Bill hearings. For instance, Dr. Bostwick H. Ketchum, president of the Ecological Society of America and associate director of the Woods Hole Oceanographic Institution, testified, "In the long run, the very survival of mankind may depend on what we do today and in the near future to use and exploit our environment." As I have repeatedly emphasized, the crisis of air pollution is seriously complicated by the fact that chemical changes occur

Chicago Tribune Photo

in the atmosphere which we understand only slightly and which we have little power to control or even detect. This is true with relatively simple pollutants such as automobile exhausts. Think of the implications for air pollution of nuclear testing. Two years after water in the western Pacific was contaminated by radioactive fallout, clams were found to contain large concentrations of the radio isotope, Cobalt-60.

Scientists tell us that Cobalt-60 is not produced by atomic fission. It must have been produced by the action of radiation on some chemical in the water. These findings involving Pacific Ocean clams showed that dangerous new chemicals can be accumulated in the tissues of animals up to several million times the concentration in the surrounding water. In the light of such findings, think of the implications for our environment if we were to adopt the suggestion to use nuclear explosions to dig a canal across Central America.

Let us take a brief look at what our governments

Scientists cannot predict accurately just how long the atmosphere will be able to absorb the deadly fumes from millions of trucks, jets and cars.

Air pollution does $10 to $12 billion damage every year.

are presently doing about air pollution. Many of our cities and some counties have developed local air pollution programs. These started out as "smoke control programs," but we know now that the problem is much more complex than controlling local smoke.

Relatively few states have strong anti-pollution programs. The federal government's role in air pollution consists of making grants to local air pollution agencies so they can operate their own programs pretty much as they please. While leaving full responsibility for air pollution control programs at the state and local level, the Clean Air Act did put the federal government clearly in charge of reducing automobile exhaust pollution. It authorized federal standards for systems to control auto exhausts beginning with 1968 models.

The most obvious regional air pollution problem is the New York City, New Jersey, Connecticut area. What can the suburban communities in New Jersey and Connecticut do about the mushroom-like cloud of pollution which often envelops Manhattan and all but obliterates the sun on some occasions? What can

city air pollution authorities in Chicago do about the suffocating pollution pouring out of steel mills in that giant, three-state industrial complex at the southern end of Lake Michigan?

The number one reform needed in our national air pollution program is the immediate development of regional governmental authorities to fight air pollution on the scale that it occurs. Our present Clean Air Act offers financial incentives to so-called regional programs. But the mere linking of two communities, which is sufficient to qualify under the law, does not create a regional program. We need regional programs involving several cities and several states — boundary lines drawn to suit the air pollution problem which exists, not to conform to other lines of the map. These regional programs should encompass an entire geographic area which has a common air pollution problem.

If offering financial incentives does not get this job done, then the federal government should have the authority to establish the regional units which we need made up of representatives from existing units of government. A regional program involving the

The Chicago Air Pollution Patrol investigates a complaint.

great industrial complex of Chicago, Gary, Hammond and Whiting, Indiana, would provide an excellent model for the development of truly coordinated and comprehensive air pollution control and waste disposal systems. In addition to regional air pollution control units, we need to take another step forward and give the federal government authority to set air quality standards and emission standards. Few communities have the facilities to develop proper standards. And private industry should not be faced with widely differing standards from city to city. This creates the old problem of competitive disadvantage and encourages some industries to threaten to move away if tough standards are set.

The rationale for federal standards on auto exhausts is that cars move from state to state and the problem is the same everywhere. But the smoke from a huge electric generating plant in New Jersey moves into New York just as autos do, and the problem of controlling such emissions is the same regardless of where they originate. Motor vehicles account for sixty per cent of all air pollution. In some cities, they produce up to ninety per cent. The three alternatives most often considered are the gas turbine, the electric and the steam engines. The steam engine and the gas turbine have emission characteristics much lower than the internal combustion engine. The electric engine produces no hazardous fumes. The social overhead this country

has borne because of the combustion engine has been steep. The dollar cost of the internal combustion engine ranges up to $15 billion a year. As more is learned about the effects of the engine, other damages are discovered and the overhead increases even more.

In California alone, crop losses attributable to chemical pollutants are in the neighborhood of $6 to $10 million each year. Smog also attacks rubber, textiles, dyes and other materials, in addition to depositing coats of grime wherever it touches down. It even affects the weather in subtle and highly significant ways through modification of the earth's energy balance by causing changes in the distribution and quality of radiant energy and through alteration of the physical processes of condensation and precipitation. More importantly, automobile pollutants affect human beings. Carbon monoxide reduces the capacity of the blood to carry oxygen from the lungs to body tissues. Unburned hydrocarbons are possibly carcinogenic. Oxides of nitrogen are a major cause of smog and can be toxic, even fatal in high concentrations. Oxidants such as ozone can cause eye irritations and adverse respiratory effects. Scientists are still trying to determine the toxicity of lead compounds and other pollutants thought to be harmful to humans. Collectively, these chemicals increase the incidence of cancer, emphysema, chronic bronchitis, asthma and possibly the

59

Downtown Los Angeles on a clear day in 1956 contrasts vividly with a smoggy day when the haze and smoke are trapped three hundred feet above the ground by a temperature inversion.

Chicago Tribune Photo

Chicago: January 15, 1970, looking southwest from the Tribune Tower.

common cold. The Los Angeles County Medical Association recently warned that on days when smog covers that city, parents should limit outside activities of their children because of danger to their lungs.

The air pollution problem has reached crisis proportions. In London, as far back as 1952, a thermal inversion caused upwards of four thousand deaths.* The wind has taken a holiday in other cities including New York City in 1953 and 1966, St. Louis and Chicago more recently, threatening further thousands of lives. Even now, the nation's steel mills are less than one-third effective in controlling their air discharges of particulate matter. The petroleum refineries have controls that are only sixty per cent effective. The level of particulate control in the nation's municipal incineration, not including open burning, is only twenty per cent. The goal is clear. The states must set standards which will be satisfied not by excuses but by clean air. Deadlines must be set for polluters to act — and if these deadlines are not met, polluters must be taken to court as the Air Quality Act of 1967 requires.

Citizens should take advantage of the opportunity to speak out. You can be sure that those whose concern isn't clean air but profit, will speak their piece at every turn in the standard setting and enforcing processes. There is no respite in sight, unless we take drastic steps now to control the wastes of our society. We know the dimensions of the job cut out for us. We know too that for the most part, our technology is more than adequate to clean up our air. The real challenge is not technological — but social and political. Implementation of the Air Quality Act is now getting underway. The federal government has issued criteria for two of the most important types of pollutants, sulfur oxides and particulate matter. Fifty-seven air quality regions have been selected and designated by the federal government. These regions involve all fifty states and more than seventy per cent of the total United States urban population.

Now it is up to the states to respond. Congress and the federal government also have the continuing responsibility to provide adequate funds to carry out provisions of the program. Our record in this regard must be better in the future than it has been in the past. Large gaps have appeared in past years be-

tween authorizations and appropriations of funds for federal pollution control efforts. The same scientist who can cleanse instruments to spend germ free years in space must develop methods to end the present pollution of air, water and the land here on earth and recycle and reuse our immense wastes. Thousands of scientists are making clear their concern that science and technology find a new relevance and a new role in modern society. The driving force of this new concern is the insistence that we establish national priorities that ring true with the American purpose and the American dream. As an example, our nation is pre-eminent in the world scientifically and technologically — but if we continue to float this program with the same or even decreased appropriations, we are running a great risk of throwing away that leadership.

When we look at the immensity of just our environmental problems and then at the number of scientists and the amount of money available in this area, it is evident our efforts are simply inconsequential. If we act — and win — we will be setting a new bench mark for progress. It won't be gross national product. It won't be mere quantity. It will be achieving quality of life for America. That is where we've got to put our money and our talent. That is the new challenge for science and technology. That is the new job for our society.

* The British government in 1956 adopted regulations requiring a subsidized changeover from coal to fuel oil for heating. Although there was another "killer smog" in 1962 during which 1,300 persons died, by the end of 1969, household chimneys smoked only thirteen per cent as much as they did in 1956, and industrial smoke was only eighteen per cent as great.

7

Pesticides:
The Warning Signs Are Clear

A recent grim scenario from a noted ecologist, Dr. Paul Ehrlich, projects the end of the oceans as a significant source of life in ten years. Mass starvation of mankind follows, then war.

Dr. Ehrlich says if present trends continue, such a disastrous end to life on earth could be perilously near. Not surprisingly, pesticides were a key part of Dr. Ehrlich's setting for disaster. As the first dramatic danger signal of the threat to life in the sea, the ecologist cites the report in 1968 that DDT slows down photosynthesis in marine plant life.

In his article in *Ramparts* magazine, Dr. Ehrlich spells out the implications: "It was announced in a short paper in the technical journal, *Science*, but to ecologists it smacked of doomsday. They knew that all life in the sea depends on photosynthesis, the chemical process by which green plants bind the sun's energy and make it available to living things. And, they knew that DDT and similar chlorinated hydrocarbons had polluted the entire surface of the earth, including the sea."

Events moved inexorably from that point on in the Ehrlich scenario, with pesticides continuing to play a major role. Through the present, all events he cites are fact. For the future, he bases his conjecture on current trends. Is it implausible to project the end of the oceans and man in ten years?

There have been too many "implausibles" or "impossibles" in this century that have come true: World War I, World War II, the atomic bomb, the hydrogen bomb, the war in Vietnam, the riots in American cities and universities, the assassination of a President, a candidate for President, and an international civil rights leader. One can readily understand the perceptive comment of Nobel Prize-winning biologist Dr. George Wald that today's youth are the first generation that believes, and with good reason, that there may be no future.

Only a short time ago any one discussing our environmental problems could not have thought to include pesticides as a major threat. Like other technological innovations, pesticides have come into being and then into mass use with stunning speed.

DDT was first formulated in 1874. But its properties as an insecticide were not discovered and put into use until World War II. Almost immediately, DDT became known as the miracle insecticide that helped control tropical disease and win the war. Since then, thousands of millions of pounds of DDT and other synthetic pesticides have been applied to millions of acres to regulate economic plant and animal populations, to protect food and fiber crops, reduce vectors of disease and abate pest nuisances. Billions upon billions of pests have fallen victim to their dust, spray and powder.

But new strains of pests developed with increased resistance to DDT and other common pesticides. Too often, instead of seeking more effective, more selective means of pest control, the reaction of many users has been to apply more, perhaps two, three, ten times as much to overcome the pest's newly attained resistance. Today, nearly 900 million pounds of pesticides, including insecticides, herbicides, fungicides, rodenticides and fumigants, are sold annually in the United States alone, more than four pounds for every American. Last year, the sales of pesticides increased some ten per cent over the previous year, and by 1985, it is estimated that they will increase another sixfold.

Reports indicate that about one acre of every ten in America is treated with an average of nearly four pounds of pesticides every year. And in a little over twenty-five years, DDT and other pesticides have been spread by the soil, wind, the tide and the chain of life itself to the farthest reaches of the earth. This and other highly persistent, mobile pesticide compounds are now one of the most easily distinguishable marks of the presence of man. And with

Opposite: The dangers of pesticides are clearer every day.

Pesticide residues were found in four out of sixteen Adelie penguins tested.

these same compounds man could reach all parts of the earth.

In 1963, two U.S. scientists hypothesized that the entire globe may already have been contaminated by DDT. To find out they went to Antarctica. If any area of the world were to be free of pesticide residue, it would be that isolated continent, where there are no pests, few animals or plants, and where the nearest pesticide use is thousands of miles away. The scientists found pesticide residues in four of sixteen Adelie penguins they tested, four of sixteen Wedell seals and fifteen of sixteen skuas, a sea bird. The evidence was inescapable: Worldwide pesticide contamination was confirmed.

Another scientist who measured residues in the Antarctic snow melt estimated that over the last two and one-half decades, about 2,600 tons of DDT could have accumulated in the Antarctic snow and ice. Scientists have yet to discover exactly how DDT and other pesticides have spread so far so fast. But some things are clear: DDT, with a half life of ten years, is remarkably hard to break down, especially in the natural environment where nature has not developed the means to decompose this synthetic compound. And pesticides such as DDT and Dieldrin are highly mobile, able to travel through the environment by any number of means.

The pesticide residues tend to concentrate to progressively higher levels when they are picked up around the globe by tiny organisms, then passed up the food chain. A well-researched example of this characteristic was documented in California. In order to control a troublesome flying insect that was hatching in a lake in that state, the water was treated with the insecticide DDD — similar to DDT — yielding a concentration of 0.02 parts per million. Plankton, which includes microscopic waterborne plants and animals, accumulated the DDD residues at five parts per million. Fish eating the plankton concentrated the pesticide in their fat levels from several hundred up to two thousand parts per million. Grebes, diving birds similar to loons, fed on the fish and died. The highest concentration of DDD found in the tissues of the grebes was 1,600 parts per million. If it were simply a case of another compound sprawling over the earth like dirt or air, there might be little cause for concern. But the implications of the pervasive accumulation are far more serious. It is obvious that an apparently harmless concentration in the bio-sphere at the lowest form of the life system gradually is reconcentrated in each step until, in the upper echelons of the food chain, the concentration of the pesticide is lethal to many creatures and already a threat to man.

Dr. Charles Wurster, Jr., an organic chemist and nationally known pesticide expert assisting the Environmental Defense Fund, likens the pesticide spread to mass use of biocides, agents which are known by scientists as "active against life." "In general, if an organism has nerves, DDT or Dieldrin can kill it," Wurster believes. He says the action of other hard, chlorinated hydrocarbon pesticides such as Aldrin, Endrin, Heptachlor and Toxaphene is similar. Thus, Wurster says, these compounds "are toxic to almost the entire animal world."

During a recent conference on pesticides in Stockholm, evidence was presented that DDT, even in very small quantities, could affect human metabolism. One of the studies cited was Russian research that indicated that workers whose jobs bring them in contact with DDT and other organochlorine pesticides were found to suffer from changes in the liver which slowed down the elimination of wastes from the body.

A major study published this summer by the National Cancer Institute found that at least eleven pesticides out of 123 chemical compounds tested induced a significantly increased incidence of tumors in laboratory animals.

While researchers have reserved judgment on whether these pesticides should be considered as a potential cause of cancer, it appears very certain that growing concern about the threat of pesticides to human health is entirely warranted. In twenty-five years, then, we have turned loose on the earth a massive dose of compounds that can cripple or kill and which are tragically indiscriminate in their attacks. When DDT is applied to do one job, it lingers and accumulates in the environment as a threat to fish, wildlife and possibly even to man.

Already the petrel of Bermuda, the bald eagle and peregrine falcon of America and the blue shell crab of the sea are each being pushed to the brink of extinction by the spread of pesticides through our environment. Like so many other environmental disasters, it is shocking that this has happened. But what is almost beyond belief is that even from the beginning the pesticide dangers were known. The fact that DDT would kill wildlife was determined in 1945, the same year the pesticide was released for civilian use. The discovery was made by wildlife biologists working in U.S. Department of Agriculture studies. From that point on, scientific concern continued to mount worldwide but, unfortunately, the debate simmered out of the public eye for almost two decades.

A dramatic turning point came in 1962 when *The New Yorker* magazine serialized a book by a lady biologist in the U.S. Department of the Interior that brought home to the public for the first time the rapidly building dangers from pesticide misuses. The book was *Silent Spring* by the late Miss Rachel Carson. Challenging the myth that pesticides were the panacea that they were being proclaimed, Miss Carson said, "As crude a weapon as the cave man's club has been hurled against the fabric of life."

Translated into thirty languages, the book was read by millions in the United States and around the world. Almost singlehandedly, it bridged the gap between the scientist and the concerned citizen which so often exists in our complex society today. In 1963, Miss Carson testified before the Senate Government Operations Committee chaired by our colleague Senator Abraham Ribicoff. Also in 1963, a report by the President's Science Advisory Committee, chaired by Jerome Weisner, concluded that the goal of our national efforts should be "elimination of the use of persistent toxic insecticides."

In the following Congress, I initially introduced legislation to ban the interstate sale and shipment of DDT. I subsequently introduced the same legislation in the ninetieth and ninety-first Congresses, and similar measures have since been introduced in the House. During the past three Congresses, no committee hearings have been held on these proposals. However, interest around the country in achieving effective pesticide controls continued to build, and there was growing citizen impatience with the failure of the state and federal agencies to act.

Yet, despite the urgent warnings and concern, our

Four birds that are being pushed
to the brink of extinction by the spread
of pesticides: the marsh hawk (*above*),
the goshawk (*right*), the petrel (*below*) and
the magnificent bald eagle (*opposite page*).

government agencies have failed miserably to respond responsibly to this massive problem. Not a single federal office has taken any significant action that would lead to the goal of "eliminating" the use of persistent toxic pesticides that was established six years ago by the Presidential committee. The fact is that the federal government has been perpetuating this grave environmental and health problem, rather than resolving it.

It was revealed late in 1969 that the U.S. Department of Agriculture, which is charged with regulating pesticide use, has been sponsoring a program with the air force and other government agencies under which 250,000 pounds of Dieldrin has been applied to fifty-six military and civilian airports across the country over the past fifteen years. This program, which has raised strenuous objections from scientists, was twice reviewed and approved by the Federal Committee on Pest Control, an inter-departmental committee.

The committee, which is billed as the regulator of federal pesticide use in the latter part of 1969, confirmed that the General Services Administration and the Office of the Capitol Architect have not even submitted their pesticide programs to the committee for review. Clearly the federal effort at regulating itself has been ineffective as has the regulation of pesticide use at large. Ironically, a number of states as well as several foreign countries have shown far greater willingness to act than the U.S. Government. DDT has been banned by the states of Michigan and Arizona, and overseas by Denmark and Sweden.* And countless cities and towns have stopped using DDT and other hard pesticides within their borders.

These recent state and local measures are a reflection of the citizen demand for action that has been building at a heartening pace. For instance, the idea of creating an Environmental Defense Fund grew out of a suit filed in April 1966, against the Suffolk

County Mosquito Control Commission by Victor J. Yannacone, Jr., a young lawyer, on behalf of his wife, Carol, and all other people of Suffolk County, Long Island. The court challenge was based on a report that a DDT dumping by commission employees was the cause of fish kill in a nearby lake.

The New York suit was successful in leading to a temporary ban on the use of DDT in Suffolk County by public agencies and gained public recognition as one of the first attempts to argue that the citizen has the right under law to protect his environment.

Then, in November 1967, the Environmental Defense Fund brought its first court action in its own name, seeking to prevent the use of Dieldrin in a Japanese-beetle control project in Michigan by the Michigan and U.S. Department of Agriculture. Several Michigan Conservation Department affidavits, including one holding that the spraying would threaten Lake Michigan's new coho salmon fishery, were disallowed on a technicality when the state

* The Wisconsin Legislature in 1969 adopted a law banning the use of DDT in the state except by petition showing no other control is possible. Administrative rulings concerning all persistent pesticides were the subject of public hearings in July, 1970, with implementation expected during the fall.

DDT has been linked to reproduction failures in certain birds including the osprey (shown in a dramatic photo above).

A study by the Bureau of Sport Fisheries found DDT in
584 of 590 samples of fish taken from rivers and lakes.

attorney general's office refused to let the department officially enter the case. The tragic results of pesticide misuse for the coho were to become evident three years later. In the Michigan suit, Yannacone got a temporary order from the State Court of Appeals to stop the Dieldrin spraying but this injunction was dissolved after a six-hour trial.

In 1968, the DDT battleground shifted across Lake Michigan to Madison, Wisconsin, where citizen groups and the Environmental Defense Fund, (EDF), joined forces in a petition asking the State Department of Natural Resources to ban the use of DDT in Wisconsin under any circumstances where the pesticide can enter world circulation patterns and further contaminate the biosphere. With EDF, the petition groups were the Citizens Natural Resources Association of Wisconsin and the Wisconsin Division of the Izaak Walton League.

In the state hearing, which began in December 1968, the alliance of concerned scientists and lawyers presented extensive testimony outlining the growing pollution of the environment by persistent pesticides in the chlorinated hydrocarbon family. Dr. Robert W. Risebrough, an environmental scientist at the University of California in Berkeley, stated that the effect of pesticides on man may be very serious. He said that man accumulates twelve parts per million of DDT in his fatty tissues before the body discharges it. He said that this is enough to stimulate enzyme production, which acts as a catalyst for bodily processes, such as digestion. Risebrough added that the death of some birds has been traced to enzyme induction by DDT, impairing their ability to reproduce.

Dr. Wurster testified on the range of pesticide residues through the world. Other witnesses have testified that DDT goes into the atmosphere along with evaporating water, builds up to extremely high levels in predator birds and animals and has caused new insect problems by killing predators that once held those insects in check. Dr. Joseph Hickey, a University of Wisconsin wildlife ecologist, said that DDT has been linked to reproduction failures of certain birds, including the eagle, the osprey and the

Research over a four-year period ending in 1968 has determined that more than 1,640,000 fish were killed by pesticide pollution in U.S. waters.

peregrine falcon. Dr. Hickey and other researchers have traced the presence of pesticide residues to a decrease in weight and thickness of the shells of eggs produced by these birds.

In related testimony, Lucille Stickel, the pesticide research coordinator of the Interior Department's Patuxent Wildlife Research Center, stated that the presence of small quantities of DDT and its derivative DDE in the diet of mallard ducks decreased eggshell thickness, increased egg breakage and decreased overall reproductive success. Although the second half of the hearings, held in the spring of 1969, was billed as the time for the defense against arguments of the environmentalists, the pesticide industry, which has promoted more pesticide use and fought new controls, made a weak defense.

Industry witnesses who were knowledgeable about the environmental impact of pesticides were few and far between. Instead, defense witnesses relied on shopworn repetitions of the past triumphs of DDT and trotted out research from a decade ago which purported to show that the health of pesticide workers was not impaired by constant exposure to the compounds. In fact, witnesses for the defense often provided environmentalists with valuable evidence to support their contentions. For example, a Shell Development Company scientist confirmed the fact that DDT does not remain in the soil, but has a great deal of mobility and persistence which enables it to infiltrate the atmosphere, the waters and the total environment. Another witness for the DDT defense, a U.S. Department of Agriculture pesticide official, admitted that his agency relies almost totally on industry claims regarding health and environmental effects.

Midway through the Wisconsin hearings, a new and dramatic confirmation of pesticide dangers was announced to Wisconsin and the nation. The U.S. Food and Drug Administration siezed 28,150 pounds of frozen Lake Michigan coho salmon because it said high DDT and Dieldrin residues had made the fish unfit for human consumption. According to the FDA, the concentration of DDT in the salmon was found to be up to nineteen parts per million, while the accumulation of Dieldrin was just short of 0.3 of a part per million, both levels

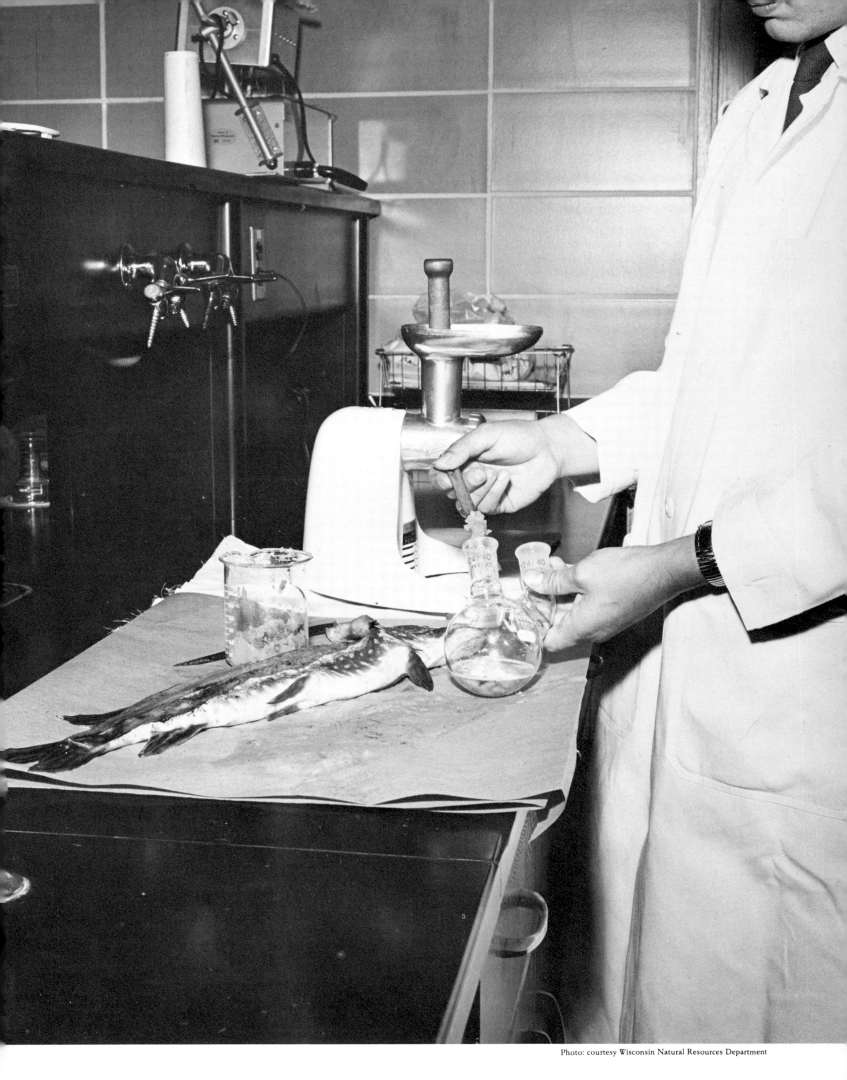

Photo: courtesy *The Milwaukee Journal*

Commercial fishermen, such as these on the Mississippi, cannot accept the reasoning that DDT is an "economic poison."

considered hazardous by the FDA and the World Health Organization.

The contamination of the coho challenges a basic foundation of the pesticide argument that has been sounded for a quarter of a century — that pesticide use is invariably an economic benefit, that is to say, an "economic" poison. One might ask the commercial fisheries who see the coho salmon as a great new opportunity in a lamprey-ravaged Great Lakes fishery whether the current pesticide approach is "economic." One might also ask the same question of the resort owners in northern Michigan who saw their business skyrocket with the introduction of the salmon in Lake Michigan in 1965.

One might ask the economic benefit question of the Michigan Department of Natural Resources, which, during the 1968 EDF suit, attempted to warn of the danger to the coho, and which has invested millions of dollars to plant coho salmon fry in Lake Michigan only to see nearly a million of the fry killed by the pesticide contamination. And, finally, one might ask the economic effects if the national recreation resource of the Great Lakes, enhanced by millions of state and federal tax dollars, is further damaged by pesticide peril to the salmon and other lake resources including the very quality of the water.

Ironically, the Lake Michigan Water Pollution Conference in 1968 was warned that the pesticide concentration was at the crisis point. W.F. Carbine, Great Lakes Regional Director for the Bureau of Commercial Fisheries, stated:

> *Lake Michigan has the highest concentration of pesticides of any of the Great Lakes, which now are only slightly below levels that are known to be injurious to man or aquatic life. . . . A continuation of high levels or an upsurge in pesticide application in the Lake Michigan Basin could increase the pesticide concentration prevailing in the open lake from the present non-lethal level to lethal value.*

The evidence is already clear that for the United States, the Lake Michigan tragedy is only the beginning. On June 17, 1969, fifty-two cases of jack mackerel caught on the West Coast were confiscated in New York by the Food and Drug Administration because of high DDT levels. The mackerel appeared to be the first ocean fish from American waters to be declared unfit for human food because of DDT. In

Fish-eating birds like the pelican
acquire high concentrations of pesticides
by eating contaminated fish.

several central and northern New York lakes, lake trout either have been eliminated, or their reproduction seriously impaired because of high pesticide levels. DDT concentrations in the lake trout of up to three thousand parts per million in the fatty tissues already have been reported.

A two-year national pesticide study completed in 1969 by the U.S. Bureau of Sport Fisheries and Wildlife found DDT in 584 of 590 samples of fish taken from forty-five rivers and lakes across the United States. The study results showed DDT ranging up to forty-five parts per million in the whole fish, a count more than nine times higher than the current Food and Drug Administration guideline level for DDT residues in fish. Residues of DDT reached levels higher than the FDA's temporary limit of five parts per million in twelve of the rivers and lakes including the Hudson in New York; the Delaware River; the Cooper in South Carolina; St. Lucio Canal and the Apalachicola in Florida; the Tombigbee in Alabama; the Rio Grande in Texas; Lake Ontario; Lake Michigan; the Arkansas and the White rivers in Arkansas; the Sacramento River in California.

Residues of Dieldrin, a pesticide even more toxic to humans than DDT, were found in excess of the 0.3 parts per million FDA limit in fifteen rivers and lakes including the Connecticut; the Hudson; the Delaware; the Savannah in Georgia; the Apalachicola; the Tombigbee; the Rio Grande; Lake Ontario; Lake Huron; the Illinois in Illinois; the San Joaquin in California; and the Rogue in Oregon. In summary, the comprehensive survey found DDT in almost one hundred per cent of the fish samples, Dieldrin in seventy-five per cent, heptachlor and/or heptachlor epoxide in thirty-two per cent and Chlorodane in twenty-two per cent.

Related research over the four-year period ending in 1968, has determined that more than 1,640,000 fish were killed by pesticide pollution in the nation's waters, the result of pesticide spills or runoff and the concentration in our waters. Millions more fish, no doubt, went unborn due to reproductive failures caused by pesticides. Laboratory research has proved that pesticide levels in water, of even the low parts per billion, can be toxic to adult fish. Levels in the low parts per trillion have been found to affect reproduction.

Already the pesticide levels in Lake Michigan, the most pesticide-polluted of the Great Lakes, are in the low parts per trillion range. And findings released in October 1969 by the U.S. Public Health Service reported the detection of pesticides in seventy-six of the seventy-nine samples of drinking water supplies around the country. Although the Public Health Service report noted that so far the pesticide levels have not exceeded recommended permissible limits, the health service was concerned. The Public Health Service said:

> The high frequency of occurrence and our lack of knowledge of the long-term health effects of this class of compounds dictate the need for increased surveillance and research as well as for increased recognition of the potential of this problem by state and local health departments.

In summary, the already massive and still accumulating evidence on pesticides makes it clear that these toxic compounds have become one of the most serious problems of our environment and are threatening even greater worldwide damage. Pesticides have concentrated to the far ends of the earth; they are killing fish and wildlife; they have inhibited fish and wildlife reproduction; high pesticide residues have pushed some fish-feeding birds and other animals to the edge of extinction; and now, there is increasing concern and evidence about the threats posed to man.

The problem of pesticides in the environment is showing up most dramatically and seriously in our rivers and lakes. Although the bulk of pesticide application is on land, the compounds, especially hard pesticides like DDT and Dieldrin, are persisting long enough to be carried by agricultural and urban runoff into water bodies. There, as I have pointed out, they enter and are concentrated through the food chain of marine life and fish-feeding birds.

This country's use of herbicides and defoliants in Vietnam is another example of a dangerous threat to the entire ecology of that southeast Asian nation. Two zoologists made a study of the ecological effects of the Vietnam War in 1969. They found, in addition to the massive bomb cratering that is turning much of the countryside into areas looking like the surface of the moon, that there is heavy damage to areas treated with herbicides to defoliate the trees and plants. In some cases, the damage appears to be permanent.

Because of the necessity of the occasional jettisoning of herbicides and spraying accidents, not all the defoliation was along the suspect jungle trail hiding places of the Viet Cong. In one residential area between Saigon and the U.S. Air Base at Bien Hoa, the scientists examined diseased mango trees and talked to a trained biologist who claimed that the trees had suffered defoliation three years previously and had not flowered or produced fruit since that time. In a preliminary report of their experiences, the zoologists describe the defoliants as having a "ghastly effect of denuding the country of growth" and related that "we consider the ecological consequences of defoliation very severe."

With the almost indifferent normal destruction of the natural resources of the world going on, it is particularly horrifying to read of wholesale premeditated destruction of plant life in vast sections of Vietnam. No one apparently knows how long it takes for the destroyed areas to return to normal. Some of the military testing of chemical-biological warfare weapons has been similarly disastrous.

There is a small island, Gruinard, off the remote northwest coast of Scotland where the British tested deadly Anthrax germs during World War II. That island is still infected and scientists believe it will stay that way for at least one hundred years. The same is true of a plot of land on the Dugway Proving Grounds in Utah and another in Alaska. Fortunately, the awareness of the magnitude of the threat facing the environment of the world is growing.

Congress recognizes the seriousness of the threat from pesticides and germ warfare tests, but has not given it the urgent attention it deserves. The problem is being dealt with in piecemeal fashion. Some limitations on chemical-biological testing are discussed; a few water quality and air pollution bills pass; and the threat to the environment remains the number one crisis facing this nation and the world.

It is difficult not to think about the kind of world the children of America inherited fifty years ago in comparison with the world the children of today face. They are being cheated of their legacy, and their children will have no legacy at all. Former Interior Secretary, Stewart L. Udall, has made the suggestion that since it will be their world, that "Young people may start picketing polluters and campaign against ugliness." The necessity for action was expressed by biologist Barry Commoner, chairman of the St. Louis Committee for Environmental Information, who warned, "We don't really know what the long-term effects of various types of environmental deterioration will be, and the kids are the guinea pigs."

Opposite: It seems evident that nothing short of a total ban on DDT will save our wildlife.

8

New Frontiers in Outdoor Recreation

Nowadays, when I go hiking along one of my favorite forest paths in northern Wisconsin, a new feeling of optimism will go with me — a feeling I hope is shared by all Americans who love the nation's outdoors. That reassurance springs from the National Trails System Act signed into law in 1968, by President Lyndon B. Johnson. Our kids aren't going to learn about the outdoors from a car window. They have to see our natural surroundings as the first settlers did to really appreciate this wonderful country.

That's why, when a hiking enthusiast buttonholed me in Washington five years ago and complained bitterly that his beloved Appalachian Trail was in danger, I became interested in a law that would protect "his trail" as well as set up a national system. It took four years, and many people, to get the job done.

Hiking trails provide the American family with perhaps the most economical, most varied form of outdoor recreation. So this new law gives us a much-needed opportunity to preserve and more widely enjoy many significant parts of our natural heritage. The National Trails System will require some years to assemble. But even a beginning represents a major breakthrough for conservation and wise outdoor recreation development. The goal is to provide all of us, no matter where we live, with easy access to a wide variety of trails suited to our tastes and needs — whether we are grandparents on a Sunday stroll, kids on bicycles or horseback, or veteran hikers. The system will move toward this objective through two major programs.

Two great trails already exist. The world-famous Appalachian Trail extends two thousand miles across the East, and the even longer, more rugged Pacific Crest Trail across the West. These continuous routes will be uniformly marked, their rights-of-way clearly defined and protected by easements or government land purchases. Essential shelters will be maintained.

The Appalachian Trail will be a foot trail. The Pacific Crest will serve hikers and horseback riders, or pack animals. No motorized vehicles are allowed — except in emergencies. The National Park Service has charge of the Appalachian Trail; the United States Forest Service, the Pacific Crest Trail. As a next step, fourteen other major scenic or historic routes are to be studied by the Bureau of Outdoor Recreation as National Scenic Trails.

This means that at long last a number of old trails, rich in natural splendor or deeply woven into the nation's history, will be saved before all of them are obliterated by the impact of our industrial society. Many are now mostly under concrete, but some remain in the back country — old, almost forgotten paths worn deep by the feet of Indian warriors, trappers or traders, or grass-covered ruts in the prairie where covered wagons once rolled.

High priority is given to developing a variety of paths for various purposes in or near our proliferating metropolitan areas. Two out of three Americans now live in urbanized communities; in thirty years it will be three out of four. As green, open space is gobbled up by highways, buildings and parking lots, the people — especially the youngsters — have less and less place to hike, jog, ride bicycles or horses, or birdwatch, study plants and animals, sketch or photograph natural surroundings. We have built fabulously expensive automobile expressways, but

Opposite: In modern America, the need for outdoor recreation facilities demands urgent attention.

we have almost completely neglected those persons who like to move on foot, even though walking and hiking are the most economical and second most popular form of public recreation.

National recreation trails are intended to meet this urgent human need. The possibilities for such trails are almost endless — if we use our imaginations and plan ahead. Our goal should be hundreds of miles of recreation trails in and around each major city. I have long believed that every American should have a place not more than an hour away from his home where he can hike to enjoy the natural environment.

These trails are to be planned by local and state governments; those which meet the standards for national recreation trails will be eligible for federal cost-sharing from the Land and Water Conservation Fund. Urban trails are relatively inexpensive and can be built quickly. A number of small-scale demonstration projects undertaken in 1966 already have produced happy results. In congested Arlington, Virginia, just across the Potomac River from Washington, D.C., bicycle riders now can escape the perils and fumes of highway traffic by using an all-weather trail which runs for several miles along a creek, through existing park land most of the way, to the river. The federal cost, matched by state and local funds, was only $48,000. In Seattle, Washington, a federal investment of $49,500, matched by the University of Washington, created a nature trail through a marshy wildlife area to an island bird sanctuary and arboretum.

The Appalachian Trail is a continuous footpath which runs along the backbone of the Appalachians from Mount Katahdin, Maine, to Springer Mountain, Georgia. Its hikers move among green, primitive surroundings much of the way, or have views of pleasant farm valleys — yet most portions of the trail are not far from great cities along its route.

Since the trail crosses private lands for about two-thirds of its length, agreements had to be maintained with landowners to preserve the right-of-way. This became increasingly difficult in recent years because of the intrusion of roads, housing and commercial developments.

There is another aspect, too. The trail owes its existence to the volunteer work of many outdoor clubs and individuals along its way. These enthusiasts, banded together as the Appalachian Trail Conference, have managed the trail, built shelters, marked it with the well-known A-over-T signs, and published maps and guidebooks. Under the new law, the Appalachian Conference will continue to be the primary guardian of the trail, and this principle of participation should be extended to all trails. People should feel that they have a stake in maintaining the trails and keeping them clean and attractive. Learning how to "brush out" a trail properly isn't difficult, and it gives one a close-up understanding of some aspects of conservation. Picking up trash is a long-lasting lesson that man shouldn't thoughtlessly desecrate the good earth. I know of young families who take responsibility for maintaining portions of the Appalachian Trail because they believe such work builds character by involving youngsters with nature, giving them a sense of man's responsibility toward his environment.

The second grand-scale model, the Pacific Crest Trail, is both a hiking and riding route for 2,300 miles from Canada to Mexico, along the high ridges of the Cascades and the Sierra Nevadas. It offers some of the most dramatic and sublime mountain landscape in the world. As four-fifths of the trail is on federally-owned lands, the right-of-way can be established easily.

The Pacific Crest Trail passes include a generous share of the continent's most verdant forests, tallest and oldest trees, highest peaks, and most breathtaking waterfalls. The unique golden trout and almost extinct giant condor call them home. Abandoned mines and old frontier towns and other relics of pioneer days still remain, according to a nationwide study in "Trails in America."

It seems probable that the first two additional national scenic trails Congress will consider will be the Potomac Heritage Trail and the Continental Divide Trail. Surveys indicate both routes are "nationally significant," and the Bureau of Outdoor Recreation is now making in-depth studies. Each trail would provide its own, distinctly different outdoor experience. The Potomac Heritage Trail would follow the banks of this history-rich river for 825 miles, from its headwaters in the mountains of Pennsylvania and West Virginia, past Washington, D.C. — where it would interconnect with a proposed system of metropolitan area trails — and on through tidewater country, still reminiscent of colonial days, to Chesapeake Bay. No other trail in America offers such a concentrated scenic, cultural, natural and historic assortment.

The Continental Divide Trail would stretch for 3,082 miles through the grandeur of the Rocky Mountains from the Canadian Border to Silver City, New Mexico. It would provide a wide range of both wilderness and western history experience, enabling

This forest trail in Camano Island State Park, Washington, preserves a memory of the past.

riders and hikers to sample majestic mountain scenery, Indian reservations, and the Spanish-flavored Southwest. The major part of the route is on federal lands.

Twelve other potential scenic or historic trails await systematic study. All of them played a part in shaping the life of this country. They are:

OLD CATTLE TRAILS — such as the Chisholm Trail — over which the herds of longhorns moved from the range of southern Texas to shipping points in Kansas.

LEWIS AND CLARK TRAIL — 4,600 miles from St. Louis, Missouri, to the mouth of the Columbia River on the Pacific. (Trail includes return by alternate route.)

NATCHEZ TRACE — first used by Indians, then traders, became the early-day route between Nashville, Tennessee, and Natchez, Mississippi, on the lower Mississippi River.

NORTH COUNTRY TRAIL — 3,170 miles, from the Appalachian Trail in Vermont through northern states to the Lewis and Clark Trail in North Dakota.

SANTA FE TRAIL — the 800-mile wagon route between Independence, Missouri, and Portland, Oregon on the West Coast.

LONG TRAIL — 250 miles, from Massachusetts through Vermont to Canada.

MORMON TRAIL — the 1,200-mile route of the exodus from Nauvoo, Illinois, to Salt Lake City.

MORMON BATTALION TRAIL — 2,000 miles from Mount Pisgah, Iowa, to Los Angeles.

KITTANNING TRAIL — across the Allegheny Mountains from Shirleysburg to Kittanning in southwestern Pennsylvania.

GOLD RUSH TRAILS — in Alaska.

This Iowa farmland offers facilities for outdoor activities.

Photo: courtesy Soil Conservation Service, USDA

EL CAMINO REAL — the King's Road in Spanish Florida.

Specific plans for this part of the national system originate with local and state governments and are just getting underway. Here I strongly believe in aggressive citizen involvement. We have done virtually nothing with recreation trails in this country, mainly because state conservation departments, with few exceptions, haven't had the imagination or vision to plan them. One state conservation director once told me, "We don't build hiking trails because we have so few hikers."

He was putting the cart before the horse. How can there be hikers unless they have some place to go? And he obviously did not realize that making it easy for people to get out into the countryside, to learn about natural resources on their feet is vital to conservation. When conservation departments are stimulated to look systematically for potential trails in their states, they will be astonished by the number and variety available. After all, a good trail doesn't take much room. For example, along the Brule River in my state are deep-worn paths left by Indians and fur traders. They are only a few feet wide and meander through the woods.

To protect such a strip of history with easements, to mark it, put it on a map, and to keep it passable is fairly simple and should not be a very expensive task. Several years ago, I made a rough study of some of the more obvious trails we might develop in

Wisconsin. When we put them on a map, it showed a network totalling three thousand miles. Running mainly along river banks, lake shores, through state and national forests, these trails would put a hiking path within reach of virtually every family in cities, suburbs and small towns.

Long, continuous trails are not essential, however. Sites for many short ones, possibly five to fifteen miles long, can be found in any state. Once developed, they become, in effect, linear parks where oncoming generations can learn the vital fabric of the earth, its vegetation and its creatures, through their own eyes, ears, hands and feet. Personally, I believe that every trail should have green collections at suitable intervals — small plantations, perhaps only an acre, where youngsters could see every tree native to their state, each one identified with a plaque giving its name and characteristics.

The National Trails System Act authorizes appropriations of $5 million for acquiring lands and easements for the Appalachian Trail, and $500,000 for these purposes for the Pacific Crest Trail, most of which already is on public land. The total investment will be relatively modest. A splendid nationwide network of all types of trails can be established for less than the cost of, say, a few hundred miles of superhighway.

The federal share of the National Trails System is to be financed from the Land and Water Conservation Fund as available and appropriated. As states complete their comprehensive outdoor recreation plans and proposals, including those for trails, they may apply for cost-sharing grants from the fund. One problem, however, is that more conservation and recreation projects have been authorized than can be readily financed by the fund. It isn't that the nation is over-committed on projects — quite the contrary. Rather, the sights of the fund have been set too low.

Still, conservationists should be optimistic. A more concerned, more constructive attitude is taking hold. I keep in mind a cold weekend one October, when I hiked over a fine new trail being completed through the Chequamegon National Forest near Lake Superior. The work was being done by a group of college students who wanted that trail for themselves and for others. Twenty-five of them invested their Saturday in trimming out brush, hauling off fallen trees and leveling hummocks. By the end of a long day, they had created a pleasant seven-mile stretch of foot path where none had been before. More of that kind of spirit can give America the trails it needs — and the trails can give us more of the America we need.

The need for outdoor recreation is one of the most demanding of urgent attention nationally in our modern American society. At the same time, the outdoor recreation industry affords the most opportunity for economic advance for people living in several parts of the nation. Many of the areas having the greatest need for jobs to replace and to supplement the shrinking economic opportunities available in agriculture, in forest products, and in mining are those having the greatest potential for recreational industries.

The lack of adequate financing for recreational enterprises is the most serious factor blocking realization of the economic development potentials in many rural areas, and in failing to meet the skyrocketing need of urban residents for more satisfactory outdoor recreational facilities. The reasons for the shortage of adequate credit are fairly simple: Many outdoor recreation enterprises involve relatively heavy investments in land, and in long-life improvements such as water impounds, ski slope grading, and so forth. Credit for such purposes needs to be offered on longer terms than are available usually for financing buildings and other types of normal business facilities.

Most recreational industry potentials are located in rural areas, where banks are usually small and other sources of credit non-existent. National banks cannot invest more than seventy per cent of their deposits in real estate loans and normally do not exceed sixty per cent. Banks prefer to make short-term personal property loans rather than the long-term real estate loans that are of such critical importance in outdoor recreation enterprise financing. And banks cannot make loans for more than eighty per cent of the appraised valuation of the property, which is not adequate to insure pace of development of outdoor recreation enterprises.

The needs for more adequate credit in order to develop the outdoor recreation potential in the Northern Great Lakes Basin undoubtedly corresponds to needs in many other rural areas throughout the country. This was spelled out by the Northern Great Lakes Regional Development Committee in a resolution adopted at its meeting in Wausau, Wisconsin, in 1965. This organization, with representatives from localities in Minnesota, Michigan and Wisconsin, is a voluntary committee of local citizens which cooperates with the U.S. Department of Agriculture in planning for the development of economic opportunities in the area.

The action of the committee initiated intensive studies and discussions on the part of community leaders in the region, with the counsel and advice of experts from the University of Wisconsin and other governmental agencies in the area concerned. On December 1, 1966, a Finance Forum on Recreational and Small Business in Northern Wisconsin was conducted at Fifield, Wisconsin. The Wisconsin members of the Northern Great Lakes Resource Development Committee played key roles in planning and conducting this public policy forum which was attended by 126 local community leaders. Its purpose was to discuss and define the problems in recreational financing, to document the needs of the industry, and to determine the most appropriate solutions.

The keynote of the forum was provided by Mr. M.J. Brunner, president of the First National Bank of Rhinelander, Wisconsin. Mr. Brunner analyzed the importance of outdoor recreation enterprise to the economic future of the north and identified the particular needs for careful economic studies and for more adequate financing. At that time, existing federal lending programs could not meet the requirements of the outdoor recreation industry.

For one thing, there was a top limit of $60,000 on loans to recreation enterprises made by the Farmers Home Administration of the U.S. Department of

81

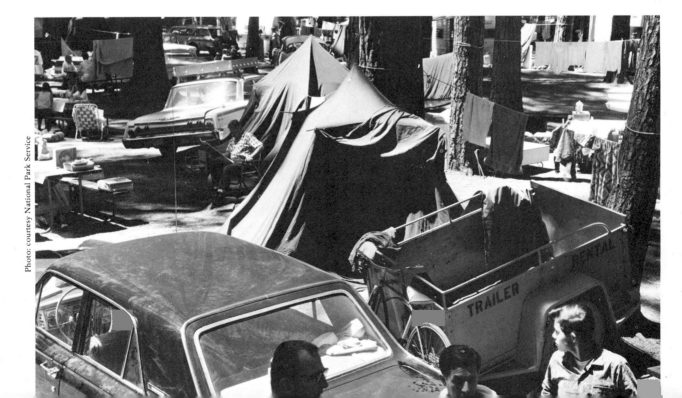

82

Close quarter camping (at Yosemite *bottom*) and close quarter city living *(left)* are two of America's ills that can be partly alleviated by acquiring more public recreation lands *(below)* and by encouraging programs like the Need Program *(far left)* which uses the natural environment as a tool to make children aware of their total environment.

Agriculture. On the other hand, the general procedure of the Small Business Administration indicated that the initial investment of its borrowers would need to be $150,000 or more. There was no source of government help readily available within the $90,000 gap in the two federal programs.

Moreover, the Farmers Home Administration was restricted to making loans only to individuals whose primary source of income was from farming and for whom outdoor recreation is a secondary source of income. The Small Business Administration, on the other hand, customarily requires that its borrowers derive their primary income from the enterprise to

be financed. Furthermore, the Farmers Home Administration did not make loans at all for recreation enterprises to small profit-making corporations or partnerships. These are excluded also from practical access to the Small Business Administration credit because of their small size.

For several reasons, the Farmers Home Administration appeared to be the logical agency to administer the new authority that is needed to extend credit to rural outdoor recreation enterprises. For one thing, the FHA was already operating an organization having local offices within convenient access to all rural communities in the country. And, it was cooperating with committees of local community leaders in screening the providing service to applicants for loans for a considerable variety of purposes. In that credit operation, the FHA program gives strong support to the principle of cooperating closely with local people — including landowners, enterprise operators, local businesses, and country bankers and other lending institutions — and directly involving them in the loans which are advanced or insured by the government.

This principle is of particular importance in credit for recreation purposes. It is extremely difficult to develop objective criteria and standards for widespread application of a type of enterprise placing such high premium upon novelty, innovation, and subjective managerial qualities. Therefore participation in the risk in the enterprise on the part of responsible local community leaders would be of great value to the government.

That would enable the government administrators to check their judgments against qualified judgments of the responsible persons in the community, who, like the government, would put some of their own money "on the line" to back up their judgment.

The bill that I introduced for that purpose — to fill the credit gap in financing economy-building recreational enterprises in rural America — provides a full recognition of this principle. Both federal government and local, responsible citizens use equal judgment in establishing these badly needed enterprises.

9

An Agenda for the 1970's

In the nearly forty years since Franklin D. Roosevelt said in his first inaugural address that "this great nation will endure as it has endured, will revive and prosper," our economy has soared to levels that no one in the 1930's could have imagined. In these past four decades, we have become the wealthiest nation on earth by almost any measure of production and consumption. As the economic boom and the post-war population explosion continued to break all records, a national legend developed: With science and technology as its tools, the private enterprise system could accomplish anything.

We assumed that, if private enterprise could turn out more automobiles, airplanes and television sets than all the rest of the world combined, somehow it could create a transportation system that would work. If we were the greatest builders in the world, we need not worry about our poor and about the planning and building of our cities. Private enterprise, with enough technology and enough profit, would manage that just fine.

In short, we assumed that, if private enterprise could be such a spectacular success in the production of goods and services, it could do our social planning for us, too, set our national priorities, shape our social system, and even establish our individual aspirations. In fact, I am sure most can recall the famous words of Charles Wilson back in the mid-1950's, when he said, "What's good for the country is good for General Motors and vice versa."

In the 1960's, the era of fantastic achievement marched on to levels unprecedented in the history of man. It was the decade when man walked on the moon — when medical magic transplanted the human heart — when the computer's mechanical wizardry became a part of daily life — and when instead of a "chicken in every pot," the national aim seemed to be two cars in every garage, a summer home, a color television set, and a three-week vacation in Europe.

From the nation of small farmers and small merchants we had been in the last century, we had become the "consumer society," with science and technology as the New Testaments and the gross national product as the Holy Grail. One might have thought we would have emerged triumphantly from the 1960's with a shout: "Bring on the next decade." But we have not. For in addition to the other traumatic national and international events, the 1960's have produced another kind of "top of the decade" list.

It has been, as we have seen in previous chapters, a decade when the darkening cloud of pollution seriously began degrading the thin envelope of air surrounding the globe; when pesticides and unrestricted waste disposal threatened the productivity of all the oceans of the world; when virtually every lake, river and watershed in America began to show the distressing symptoms of being overloaded with pollution materials.

These pivotal events have begun to warn the nation of a disturbing new paradox: The mindless pursuit of quantity is destroying — not enhancing — the opportunity to achieve quality in our lives. In the words of the American balladeer, Pete Seeger, we have found ourselves "standing knee-deep in garbage, throwing rockets at the moon."

Cumulatively, "progress, American style," adds up each year to 200 million tons of smoke and fumes, 7 million junked cars, 20 million tons of paper, 48 billion cans, and 28 billion bottles. It also means bulldozers gnawing away at the landscape to make room for more unplanned expansion. We have more leisure time, but less open space in which to spend it. There has been so much reckless progress that we now face a hostile environment. As one

Opposite: America wrongly assumed that private enterprise, with enough technology and profit, would take care of planning our cities.

84

Photo: Kit & Max Hunn from National Audubon Society

The connection between a Florida paper mill belching smoke *(above)* and masks in Chicago *(below)* grows closer every day.

Chicago Tribune Photo

measure of the rate of consumption that demands our resources and creates our vast wastes, it has been estimated that all the American children born in just one year will use up 200 million pounds of steel, 9.1 billion gallons of gasoline, and 25 billion pounds of beef during their lifetimes.

To provide electricity for our air conditioners, a Kentucky hillside is strip-mined. To provide gasoline for our automobiles, the ocean floor is drilled for oil. To provide the sites for our second homes, the shore of a pristine lake is subdivided. The unforeseen — or ignored — consequences of an urbanizing, affluent, mobile, more populous society have poisoned, scarred, and polluted what once was a beautiful land "from sea to shining sea."

The laboring man living in the shadows of the spewing smokestacks of industry certainly feels the bite of the "disposable society." And so does the commuter, inching in spurts along an expressway. And the housewife paying too much for products that begin to fall apart too soon. And the student watching the university building program destroy a community. Or the black man living alongside the noisy, polluted truck routes through the city ghetto.

There is not merely irritation now with the environmental problems of daily life — there is a growing fear that what the scientists have been saying is all too true, that man is on the way to defining the terms of his own extinction. Today, it can be said that there is no river or lake in the country that has not been affected by the pervasive wastes of our society. It also can be said that there is no clear, clean air left in the United States. The last vestige of pure air was near Flagstaff, Arizona, and that clean air disappeared six years ago.

Tomorrow? Responsible scientists have predicted that accelerating rates of air pollution could become so serious by the 1980's that many people may be forced on the worst days to wear breathing helmets to survive out-of-doors. It also has been predicted that in twenty years, many will live in doomed cities.

Dr. S. Dillon Ripley, secretary of the Smithsonian Institution, believes that in twenty-five years, between seventy-five and eighty per cent of all the species of living animals will be extinct, and other scientists, as we have noted, predict the end of the oceans as a productive resource within the next fifty years unless pollution is stopped. The United States provides an estimated one-third to one-half of the industrial pollution of the sea. It is especially ironic that, even as we pollute the sea, there is hope that its resources can be used to feed tens of millions of

A high school conservation group works at stream bank improvement.

Photo: courtesy Soil Conservation Service, USDA

hungry people.

As in the great depression, America is again faced with a crisis that has to do with material things — but it is an entirely different sort of dilemma. In effect, America has bought environmental disaster on a national installment plan; buy affluence now, and let future generations pay the price. Trading away the future is a high price to pay for an electric swizzle stick, or a car with greater horsepower. But then, the environmental consequences never have been included on the label of a product.

It is a situation we have gotten into not by design, but by default. Somehow, the environmental problems have mushroomed upon us from the blind side — although, again, the scientists knew decades ago that they were coming. What has been missing is the unity of purpose forged out of a threat to our national health or security or prestige, that we so often seem to have found only during world war. But we have begun to recognize that our security is again threatened — not from the outside, but from the inside — not by our enemies, but by ourselves. As Pogo so quaintly put it: "We have met the enemy and they is us. . . ."

Growing student environmental concern is a striking new development. As a dramatic indication of the degree the new citizen concern has reached Congress, a daily average of 150 constituent requests on environmental questions is coming into the Legislative Reference Service in the spring of 1970. This is a rate second only to that for crime. The rising citizen attendance at public hearings on polluters, the letters that are pouring into congressional offices — all are indicating a vast new concern.

In the *Congressional Record*, the amount of environmental material inserted in the first six months of 1969 by Senators and Congressmen was exceeded only by material on the issue of Vietnam. Congress, in 1969, took the major initiative of appropriating $800 million in federal water pollution control funds, nearly four times the request of the present and previous administrations. And environmentalists across the country have been heartened by the fact that the President will devote major attention to the environmental crisis as he remarked in the State of the Union message. All conservationists applauded the President's interest and commitment.

In short, I believe that today, in 1970, we are at a watershed in the history of the struggle in this country to save the quality of our environment. With the massive new coalition of interests that is now forming, which includes the urbanite and the student, it is possible to wage war on our environmental problems and win. In any such effort the continued commitment of millions of people is the most essential resource of all.

But, lest anyone be misled or caught unaware, this war will be lost before it is begun if we do not bring other massive resources to it as well. A victory will cost decades and tens of billions of dollars. Just to control pollution, it will take $275 billion by the year 2000. Although that sounds like a lot of money, it will be spent over the next thirty years and is equivalent to the defense expenditure for the next four years.

More than money, restoring our environment and establishing quality on a par with quantity as a goal of American life will require a reshaping of our values, sweeping changes in the performance and goals of our institutions, national standards of quality for the goods we produce, a humanizing and redirection of our technology, and greatly increased attention to the problem of our expanding population. Perhaps most of all, it will require on the part of the people a new assertion of environmental rights and the evolution of an ecological ethic of understanding and respect for the bonds that unite the species, man, with the natural systems of the planet Earth.

The ecological ethic must be debated and evolved by individuals and institutions on the terms of man's interdependence with nature. Institutions such as our churches and universities could be of important assistance in providing increased understanding of these ethical considerations. Such an ethic, in recognizing the common heritage and concern of men of all nations, is the surest road to removing the mistrust and mutual suspicions that always have seemed to stand in the way of world peace.

American acceptance of the ecological ethic would require nothing less than achieving a transition from the consumer society to a society of "new citizen-ship" — a society that concerns itself as much with the well-being of present and future generations as it does with bigness and abundance. It is an ethic whose yardstick for progress should be: Is it good for people? American college students — thousands of whom actively attended a teach-in on the crisis of the environment April 22, 1970, (popularly called Earth Day) on hundreds of campuses — are in the forefront in expressing the terms on which we will need to meet this critical challenge.

Students, scientists, and many others are saying that we must reject any notion that progress means destroying Everglades National Park with massive airport development — or that it is progress to use the American public as an experimental laboratory for artificial sweeteners, food additives, or other products without understanding the "technological backlash" that may come from their unmeasured dangers — or that it is progress to fill hundreds of square miles of our bays and coastal wetlands, destroying natural habitat for thousands of species of fish and wildlife, polluting our waters, and in many other ways, wreaking havoc with this fragile ecological system in the name of providing new space for industry, commerce and subdivisions.

There is a great need, and growing support, for the introduction of new values in our society — where bigger is not necessarily better, where slower can be faster, and where less can be more. This attitude must be at the heart of a nationwide effort, an agenda for the 1970's, whereby this country puts gross national quality above gross national product.

1. The first item I suggest for this agenda will be the introduction of an amendment to the U.S. Constitution which will recognize and protect the inalienable right of every person to a decent environment. In its degradation of the quality of American life — in its danger to the future of man himself — I believe the environmental crisis is the greatest single threat to our pursuit of those inalienable rights — life, liberty and the pursuit of happiness — which we have recognized as a society.

The amendment will be brief. It will state:

Every person has the inalienable right to
a decent environment. The United States
and every state shall guarantee this right.

The tragedy now is that the citizen has few clear, legal or explicit Constitutional avenues that provide redress for environmental assaults on the well-being of himself, his family or his community.

Far too frequently the citizen finds himself left

with no remedy, in the face of the pollution of a lake which belongs to the public, or the poisoning of the air which he must breathe, or the shattering din which is imposed upon him with no choice. This is because, in the development of our Anglo-Saxon common law, our protections have traditionally focused on economic or personal injury, with the subordination of other damages that we are finding are just as much a threat to the quality of life.

Although I believe we must explicitly establish environmental right and protection as a fundamental doctrine of our society, it is clear that any such right, and the terms of its protection, must be enumerated in federal and state statutes and further defined in the courts.

2. As the second item for the agenda, I propose immediate action to rid America in the 1970's of the massive pollution from five of the most heavily used products of our affluent age. In each case, I am convinced that it can be done — with firm federal action to assure it. The five products are: the internal combustion engine, hard pesticides, deter-

gent pollution, aircraft pollution, and non-returnable containers.

We should, I believe, phase out the internal combustion automobile engine by January 1, 1978, unless it can meet national emission standards by that time. I already have introduced this legislation: the Low Emission Vehicle Act. It is imperative that a near pollution-free automobile be developed and put into use as quickly as possible. Present exhausts are causing up to ninety percent of the air pollution problems in some areas of the nation. This proposal also would initiate a federal research and subsidy program to find an alternative to the internal combustion engine or improve the performance of existing alternatives.

We should eliminate persistent toxic pesticides (the chlorinated hydrocarbons) by 1972. Because of the grave, world-wide environmental dangers from these long-lasting, poisonous compounds, this step was proposed as a national goal seven years ago by the President's Science Advisory Committee. There is growing agreement that the persistent pesticides

We must reject any notion that progress means destroying Everglades National Park with massive airport development.

are expendable because of less persistent substitutes and the development of other means of pest control.

A recent decision by the U.S. Department of Agriculture to eliminate all non-essential uses of DDT by the end of this year was a step forward. Yet, the pesticide industry's continued unwillingness to initiate or accept reform, coupled with the Agriculture Department's historic hesitancy to improve pesticide regulations, makes it mandatory that Congress set a deadline on banning the persistent pesticides.

Strict anti-pollution standards should be set on detergents, including a ban on their phosphorous "builders" that have contributed so much to the pollution of our lakes. Detergents are one of the major pollution problems in the country today. Six years ago, I sponsored legislation which prompted an industry changeover to a new ingredient which cut the massive mountains of foam detergents were causing on our waters. Now, another important step is needed: elimination of detergent's polyphosphate "builders" that pass through sewage treatment systems into our lakes and rivers stimulating the growth of algae.

Most recently at House committee hearings, scientists testified that non-polluting substitutes for these detergents are now within reach. Industry, however, continues to resist such a move. Congress must act to require the substitution, and, in addition, to set national standards on the water eutrophication ability, biodegradability, toxicity and health effects of detergents.

To reduce dramatically pollution from jet aircraft, we should establish a deadline of December 1972 for the installation of smokeless combustors on their engines. Industry has produced a combustor that makes jet engines smokeless and significantly cuts their pollution. At the rate the airlines have agreed to install these devices, it would take until the middle of the decade to make the changeover. It will soon be possible to install the combustors at the rate of two hundred a month, which would accomplish the changeover in two years. But the industry is refusing to do so.

With jets in the country pouring 78 million pounds of pollutants into the atmosphere each year, there is every reason for the combustors to be installed as quickly as possible. Congress should act to require this and to provide federal assistance for research to make the combustors even more effective and easier to install. Aircraft noise is another area which is urgently in need of action.

The 1960's has been a decade when pesticides and unrestricted waste disposal threatened the productivity of all the oceans of the world and when virtually every lake, river and watershed was seriously polluted.

90

City News Bureau Photo

Photo: courtesy Wisconsin Natural Resources Department

Photo: courtesy National Park Service

Photo: courtesy *The Milwaukee Journal*

Some ecologists think that when the world's population reaches eight billion, by the year 2000, the natural environment will not be able to cleanse and restore itself.

Photo: John Hendry, Jr., from National Audubon Society

Bottles, jars and cans should be eliminated from the American landscape through a combination of effluent charges, development of reusable or degradable containers, and packaging standards. In the comprehensive solid waste management legislation that already has been introduced in the 91st Congress, provision should be made for standards which will require reusable or degradable consumer product containers as soon as they are proven to be technically feasible. In addition, our solid waste control program should be financed in part by effluent charges paid by industry or packaging that will not degrade or cannot be reused. It is my conviction that the long-run answer to our solid waste problem must be a massive effort to turn our wastes into valuable new products that can be recycled into the economy.

With these five actions, we would be taking great strides toward establishing the principle that industry's responsibilities for the human and environmental effects of its products do not stop at the end of the production line. The only way to assure this is through national laws that establish performance standards, so that products will be tested and environmental and health protections built in before, not after, they reach the marketplace.

3. The third item on the agenda quality of American life should be establishing and protecting the right of every citizen to plan his family. The funds and coordination must be made available for conducting necessary research into population problems and providing family planning services. The statistics are deeply disturbing. It took until 1850 for the world population to reach one billion. By 1930, only eighty years later, that figure had doubled; and, by the year 2000, the world population is expected to reach six to eight billion. Some ecologists see that population level as the "crash point," beyond which the natural environment will not be able to cleanse and restore itself from the massive pressure of exploitation and pollution.

At the December 1969 meeting of the American Association for the Advancement of Science, there was general agreement that the world's optimum population limit already has been passed. Measured in terms of our past performance in protecting our environment the United States already is overpopulated. If we cannot manage the wastes produced by 200 million people, it will be a catastrophe when we reach 300 million as predicted within the next thirty years.

4. The fourth item on an agenda for the 1970's must be involving the citizen in environmental decision-making through new mechanisms, including establishment of new channels and forms for public participation, creation of a citizen environmental advocate agency, and creation of an environmental overview committee in Congress. As a start, industry must consult with the community on the pollution controls needed to protect and enhance the environment. It must make a full disclosure of facts before, not after, the decisions are made that affect the consumer and his environment.

Although it is ironic that it needs to be said, public participation in environmental decision-making must also be extended to our government. The sorry history is that through rhetoric, inaction and compromise with special interests, our public institutions have been accomplices in frittering away the quality of American life. The infusion of every level of government with a spirit of advocacy and environmental ombudsmanship is urgently needed, and I will propose a citizen environmental advocate agency at federal level. This independent office would represent the public interest in matters before every federal department and in the courts.

With strong support, the National Environmental Policy Act recently signed into law and a complementary proposal now pending in the Senate-House conference that would provide staff support should be major steps forward in achieving in the White House an independent overview of federal activities as they affect the American environment. Hopefully, one of the most frequently used provisions of the National Environmental Policy Act will be the one which makes available to the public the agency reports required where a federal program or project would significantly effect the environment.

Finally, Congress itself could profit greatly by the establishment of a non-legislative environmental committee that would provide all committees with a continuing assessment of the state of the environment and of federal environmental activities.

5. A fifth item on an environmental agenda for the

We are at a watershed in the history of the struggle in the United States to save the quality of our environment.

1970's should be the launching of a broad-scale effort to halt the pollution of our sea. Municipalities and industries must be required to halt their wholesale dumping of wastes into the ocean environment. But man's activities in the oceans have their most immediate effect on our very limited continental shelves, the most productive areas of the sea. If this sensitive environment is destroyed, sea life will diminish rapidly and a major source of food protein will be lost in a world that is searching for resources to feed its exploding population. In a glimpse into the future, the report of the President's Panel on Oil Spills predicts that we can expect a Santa Barbara-scale pollution incident once a year by 1980, if offshore oil development continues at the present rate.

To meet this problem, Congress should declare a moratorium on further outer continental shelf development until ground rules are established. Recreation, esthetics, fishery resources, and natural ecology must not be sacrificed in the interest of mineral and other development.

A high-level commission should be established and given the two-year task of conducting an inventory of our off-shore resources and recommending criteria by which we can achieve a harmonious relationship with the ocean environment. Upon the

Above: To provide electricity for our air conditioners,
a hillside is defaced and scarred by strip mining.

establishment of criteria, the moratorium would be lifted.

6. The sixth item on the agenda should be the establishment of an environmental education program which will make the environment and man's relationship to it a major interdisciplinary subject of study at every level of public education. No country can maintain its vigilance in protecting its environment without a broad education for understanding of man's relationship to his land, air, water, and to other living creatures. To help achieve this, I introduced the Environmental Quality Education Act in November 1969. A companion bill was introduced in the House. The legislation would provide support for the development of new environmental education curricula from pre-school through college, adult education and community programs.

7. As a seventh item for an environmental agenda, we must utilize the billions of dollars a year that could be made available on completion of the Interstate Highway System to provide new transportation alternatives including mass transit in our polluted, congested, highway-choked urban areas. This year about $3.3 billion of the $4.4 billion administered by the highway trust fund will be spent on the Federal Interstate System, which is scheduled for completion in the mid-1970's.

Instead of being used to lay new blankets of asphalt and concrete from coast to coast in another round of massive highway building, as has already been suggested, the Interstate Highway portion of the fund that could be made available in 1975 must be put to work alleviating the Gargantuan transportation problems of our American cities. A major emphasis of those funds should be the provision of adequate mass transit systems, as well as developing and refining other transportation alternatives.

8. As an eighth item, a national policy on land use must be delineated and implemented that will halt the chaotic, unplanned combination of urban sprawl, industrial expansion and air, water, land and visual pollution that is seriously threatening the quality of life of the major regions of the nation. The nation-wide land-use policy must comprise and effectively use all the tools available to federal, state and local governments to establish rational planning, management and controls.

Such a policy must deal with the massive strip-mining operations that are ravaging and polluting vast acreages; the reckless draining and filling of wetlands that are destroying wildlife habitats and polluting vital coastal and inland areas; the helter-skelter development of our coastal and inland lakes shoreline that is eliminating a vital national asset from any future possible use; the widespread land erosion caused by urbanization that is bringing

95

about silting in and the additional pollution of our rivers and lakes; and the disruption of communities and destruction of marshlands and other scenic and naturally valuable areas that are caused by our gigantic highway program, where building in the fastest, cheapest "point to point" fashion has invariably been the rule, despite the consequences.

I should add that an integral part of our land resource and environmental heritage is the national park, lakeshore and seashore system that we have established over the past decades. In this area, we have fallen tragically short of carrying out the congressional intention of providing $200 million a year for the Land and Water Conservation Fund through 1973. Land purchase for our national parks and other federal wildlife and recreation areas is critically dependent on this fund. Yet, for last year, only $124 million was sought and appropriated. Meanwhile, outer-continental-shelf-oil revenues, intended to bring the fund to a $200-million-a-year level, have been accumulating in trust year after underfunded year, unappropriated and unspent. It is urgent that this year we provide not only the annually authorized $200 million, but the additional $164.5 million now waiting in trust.

9. A ninth item must the establishment of a national minerals and resources policy. Vital resources already are being exhausted because of our fantastic rate of consumption and our indiscriminate national waste. In addition, the extraction of our natural resources for our raw material has more often than not been done in such a way as to wreak violent and lasting environmental destruction.

A part of this national policy must be replacing the U.S. mining law of 1872 with a modern system of mineral leasing. The 1872 law is a major obstacle to wise and effective land management in a world where it is imperative to have the best kind of multiple use management. The present policy, based on that antiquated law, gives blind priority to mineral resources and makes any consideration of wildlife, recreation, esthetic or urban land values impossible. I have introduced legislation to establish a modern mineral leasing system, and a companion bill has been introduced in the House.

10. As a tenth and highly important item, America must establish a national air and water quality policy and commitment which will restore and enhance the quality of these critical natural resources. Our dirtied rivers and poisoned air are dramatic evidence of the desperate need to take

Yosemite National Park *(above)* and Snap Jack Lake in Ottawa National Forest *(right)* deserve to be saved.

action on a national, unprecedented scale.

The duel funding of present pollution control programs to close the environmental money gap is a fundamental and urgent requirement of national policy. Despite the Congressional initiative last year in federal water pollution control aid, our national water quality program still faces the danger of total collapse. While the federal aid has been trickling into the critical municipal sewage treatment program in the millions of dollars, applications for aid from cities and towns across the country are in the billions.

In this perilous situation, it is essential that we appropriate the full $1.2 billion authorized for the federal water pollution control program grants-in-aid for sewage treatment plants for the fiscal year 1971. Other means of long-range financing are being considered but we cannot afford a delay in already-authorized water quality funding while the alternatives are being debated.

A national air and water quality policy must also dramatically expand our present programs of research and development for finding ways to neutralize, dispose of, and recycle all wastes, and all governmental units and all industries and municipalities must be required to comply with the highest state of the art in treating their wastes. We must also require that as new, more effective pollution control equipment is developed, it be installed immediately and as a matter of course.

11. The eleventh item on an agenda for the 1970's must be the creation of a non-partisan national environmental political action organization, with state and local organizations providing the foundation. The organization will give the public the day to day involvement that is essential to achieving environmental solutions.

Our efforts to meet a broad-gauged agenda such as I have outlined above will require a vast increase in spending for environmental programs. At least $20 to $25 billion per year over present expenditures is essential. A major portion of this could come from existing sources of revenues by reordering national priorities diverting funds to environmental programs. New resources also must be tapped.

As we have indicated previously, a radical reduction in the level of our Vietnam involvement and an elimination of unnecessary defense expenditures will result in substantial savings which could be tapped for environmental programs, among other dramatic needs. Normal economic growth will also produce more revenue which can be earmarked for improving our surroundings.

A casual look at the deterioration that has come about over the past thirty years reveals what could be a frightening prologue to a disaster of inestimable dimensions if the accelerating rate of the environmental crisis continues. It is not, however, a trend that is impossible to reverse. If we have the will, the environmental challenge can be met. But in doing so, it will take significant modifications in our way of life. It will mark the beginning of a period when all of the institutions of our society — social, political, and economic — must readjust their philosophical attitudes toward man's relationship to his environment and all other living creatures.

Our environmental problems are man-made — the solutions must be man-made as well.